THE PHYSICIAN AND HIS PRACTICE

The Physician and His Practice

EDITED BY

Joseph Garland, M.D.

Editor, *The New England Journal of Medicine*

LITTLE, BROWN AND COMPANY

Boston • Toronto

LIBRARY OF CONGRESS CATALOG CARD NO. 54–10956

Published September 1954
Reprinted February 1955
Reprinted September 1955
Reprinted April 1956

Published simultaneously in Canada
by Little, Brown & Company (Canada) Limited

PRINTED IN THE UNITED STATES OF AMERICA

Contributors

JOHN ALAN APPLEMAN, A.B., M.A., J.D.
Member of the Bar Associations of Illinois, District of Columbia, Kentucky, United States Supreme Court, and Tax Court

DONNELL W. BOARDMAN, M.D.
Instructor in Medicine, Boston University Medical School; Assistant in Medicine, Massachusetts Memorial Hospitals

ULRICH R. BRYNER, M.D.
Past President, American Academy of General Practice; staff of Dr. W. H. Groves L.D.S. Hospital, Salt Lake City

ROBERT W. BUCK, A.M., M.D.
Secretary, Massachusetts Medical Society; formerly Chairman, Library Committee of Tufts College Medical School

C. SIDNEY BURWELL, M.D., LL.D., S.D.
Research Professor of Clinical Medicine, Harvard Medical School; Physician, Peter Bent Brigham Hospital, Boston; Visiting Physician, Boston Lying-in Hospital; formerly Dean of the Faculty of Medicine, Harvard University

DONALD M. CLARK, M.D.
Physician to Phillips Academy, Andover, Mass.; surgical staff, Monadnock Community Hospital, Peterborough, N.H.

ARTHUR C. DeGRAFF, M.D.
Samuel A. Brown Professor of Therapeutics, New York Uni-

versity College of Medicine; Visiting Physician, Bellevue Hospital, New York City

PAUL GITLIN
Member, New York Bar Association

HENRY F. HOWE, M.D.
General practitioner in Cohasset, Mass.; former President, Norfolk South District Medical Society

EDWIN P. JORDAN, M.D.
Executive Director, American Association of Medical Clinics

ALFRED KRANES, M.D.
Clinical Associate in Medicine, Harvard Medical School; Physician, Massachusetts General Hospital

KATHRYN L. McCABE, A.B., R.N.
Former President, Woman's Auxiliary to the Massachusetts Medical Society

LELAND S. McKITTRICK, M.D.
Clinical Professor of Surgery, Harvard Medical School; Surgeon-in-chief, New England Deaconess Hospital; former President, Massachusetts Medical Society

WALTER B. MARTIN, M.D.
Chief Medical Consultant, De Paul Hospital, Norfolk, Va.; Medical Consultant, United States Public Health Hospital, Norfolk, Va.; President, American Medical Association

JAMES HOWARD MEANS, M.D.
Physician to Massachusetts Institute of Technology; formerly Chief of Medical Services, Massachusetts General Hospital; Jackson Professor of Clinical Medicine, Emeritus, Harvard University

Contributors

JOHN A. POND
Director of Purchasing, University of Colorado and University of Colorado Medical Center

LOUIS J. REGAN, M.D., LL.B.
Professor of Legal Medicine, College of Medical Evangelists; Professor of Forensic Medicine, University of Southern California

BERTRAM T. UREN
Professional Management Consultant

Contents

Foreword   xi

1 EVOLUTION OF THE DOCTOR, by C. Sidney Burwell   3

2 FAMILY AND COMMUNITY RELATIONS, by Henry F. Howe   14

3 THE DOCTOR'S WIFE, by Kathryn L. McCabe   25

4 CHOICE OF OPPORTUNITIES, by James Howard Means   38

5 GENERAL MEDICINE, by Donald M. Clark   51

6 SPECIALTY PRACTICE, by Leland S. McKittrick   67

7 GROUP PRACTICE, by Edwin P. Jordan   77

8 DOCTOR AND HOSPITAL, by Alfred Kranes   89

9 MEDICAL ORGANIZATION, by Walter B. Martin   103

10 COMMUNITY MEDICAL RESOURCES, by Henry F. Howe   116

11 READING AND WRITING, by Robert W. Buck   130

12 LABORATORY FACILITIES, by Donnell W. Boardman   139

13 DRUGS AND MEDICAL SUPPLIES, by Arthur C. DeGraff   157

14 THE OFFICE AND RELATED BUSINESS ASPECTS, by John A. Pond   167

15 AUXILIARY SERVICES, by Ulrich R. Bryner   177

16 OFFICE RECORDS, by Bertram T. Uren   191

17 ACCOUNTING PRACTICES — THE INCOME TAX, by Paul
       Gitlin   205

18 ECONOMIC SECURITY, by John Alan Appleman   226

19 MEDICINE AND THE LAW, by Louis J. Regan   245

     Index   261

Foreword

THE PHYSICIAN AND HIS PRACTICE has been planned primarily as a source book of information regarding his career rather than as a detailed guide for the young doctor, who, his internship, residency, or military service completed, contemplates the fascinating fields that his training has laid open to him. It is a book that practitioners of longer standing may also find of value as they review their methods of practice, their material equipment, and the resources of the communities in which they live and work.

A proper emphasis is placed on the character and personality of the physician and the standards that are expected of him — and of his wife — in relation to the two important circles in which they move: the intimate family circle and the larger community one. The fields that medicine now encompasses are here defined, with discussions of the various types of activities that they offer, the necessity of hospital affiliations, the place of organization and organizations in the profession, and the physician's need for continued study — for gaining knowledge and for imparting it. Like Chaucer's clerk, gladly should he learn and gladly teach.

Certain chapters are devoted to the business considerations of medical practice, for every profession must be conducted in a businesslike manner if he who professes it is to make an adequate living, and if he who invokes its benefits is to get value received. One of the great impediments to the establishment of good public relations in medicine is that the physician too often fails to appreciate the importance of conducting the business of his profession in a clear and orderly fashion, acceptable to himself, to his patients, and to the tax collector.

Consonant with the plan of the book is the important point that it makes no attempt to reveal the one correct answer to each obvious question. Overlapping of material will be found, which, while it might have been avoided, need not be considered undesirable, for differing points of view can be held by different persons in different localities. Human experience does not often supply a single correct answer to the questions that it asks.

Here is presented, then, not a homogeneous text flowing with smooth consistency from the disciplined pen of a medical master mind. Rather is it a collection of essays by a number of authorities, each in his own field, each making his original contribution to the understanding if not always to the immediate solution of the special problems on which he writes.

Advice is given on many matters, it is true, but as often as not other questions are suggested that the reader must answer for himself. For even as he follows the rules the physician must plan his own strategy.

The helpful advice of Dr. Austin Smith, editor of the *Journal of the American Medical Association,* and of Dr. Chester S. Keefer, Wade Professor of Medicine at Boston University School of Medicine and special assistant to the Secretary of Health, Education and Welfare, and of others whose assistance has been freely asked and freely given, is gratefully acknowledged.

JOSEPH GARLAND, M.D.

August, 1954

THE PHYSICIAN AND HIS PRACTICE

1

Evolution of the Doctor

by C. Sidney Burwell

THESE PAGES are written for those who are beginning a career in medicine. It is my belief that such a career is a better way of life than any other for those who really have their hearts in it. It is therefore a particular pleasure to write an introductory chapter to such a book as this, which will be read by those whose character and accomplishments will determine the nature and quality of medicine in the decades immediately ahead.

Medicine has a distinguished past that goes back to the beginning of recorded history, and great figures have illuminated the field of medicine at successive stages of its development. If one contemplates the medicine of the Hippocratic era some twenty-three hundred years ago, one is impressed with certain familiar aspects. The physicians of that day were students of disease, and within the limitations of the methods available attempted to observe the manifestations of disease and to chart its course. They were attentive also to the need of their patients for reassurance and understanding. However, the fundamental theories of physiology were so different that their thoughts about causation and mechanism were different from those of today. I do not propose to discuss the physiological doctrines of the Hippocratic era, but to make a great leap over the centuries and consider briefly some of the developments in medicine during the last three hundred years. This period may be called the modern period of medi-

cal history. On the developments of this relatively short era are
founded many of our current concepts about the basis of health
and the nature, cause, and management of disease.

In many senses, William Harvey's book (*An Anatomical Disquisition on the Motion of the Heart and Blood in Animals*), published in 1628, may be considered as a cornerstone of modern
physiology. Harvey's great book was an advance, and a revolu-
tionary one, in the knowledge of one system of the body, namely,
the circulation. It was much more than that. These resourceful
and beautifully designed experiments led to a succession of discoveries and also served to establish a general method for furthering the advance of medical knowledge.

During succeeding centuries knowledge of physiology expanded by the experimental method used by Harvey, as well as
by other means. The anatomical basis of disease was studied by
morbid anatomists. To recognize structural changes before death,
various methods for exploring the body during life were developed. For example, percussion, auscultation, and X-ray examination were devised and applied, and assisted in making it possible
to describe disease in living patients in terms of alterations in
morphology. The early nineteenth century may be thought of as
a period in which there developed a so-called "clinicopathological"
concept of disease. We think of Morgagni, Laennec, and Osler as
examples of this school. But the development of modern medicine
was not as simple as this sounds. At the very same time that these
morphological concepts (still very useful) were being applied,
physicians were also working to describe disease in terms of alter-
ation in the *function* of organs and body systems. This concept of
disease in terms of physiology and chemistry expanded rapidly,
even explosively, during the nineteenth century, and most of the
ideas now serving medicine are to be found in the literature of
that great period. We may think of Cohnheim, MacKenzie, and
Peabody as exemplifying this manner of thought.

Also during this period there was growing up new knowledge

of the causes of disease. The growth of bacteriology put emphasis on specific etiology. Subsequent thinking tends to apply a broader concept in which we visualize organisms of diverse genetic make-up reacting to a complex environment. Among the environmental factors that injure or put stress on the organisms, we recognize many varieties, including the psychologic.

While these kinds of descriptions (morphologic, etiologic, physiologic) were being applied to an understanding of disease processes and disease manifestations, there were fortunately individuals who were studying the natural history of disease more broadly. The writings of Sydenham (in the late seventeenth century) remind us of those of Hippocrates. Both these ancestors of modern medicine had capacity to study patients and their diseases systematically and patiently and to record their observations. They set us examples of the unprejudiced scrutiny of phenomena, recorded without premature judgment of their significance, and they taught us to think of disease in terms of its course and its evolving pattern.

All of these diverse points of view have helped our progress to the modern degree of understanding disease. The twentieth century has seen an enormous and almost explosive increase in the knowledge of physiology and its sister biochemistry, which has resulted in great technical advances. In some areas of medicine these have reached the stage where the knowledge of disease can be translated into effective treatment or even into effective prevention. This has not been the result of following any single road in medicine. It rests on a variety of approaches and upon progress in many fields.

The technical advances of the last three hundred years give this present and fortunate generation of physicians incomparably more capacity to preserve health and control disease than was possessed by any of their predecessors. This being so, their responsibilities are correspondingly greater, and for that reason it is necessary to consider some of the factors, other than available knowledge and technic that affect the *performance* of doctors in their work with individual patients in a modern community.

This may be said another way. What are the factors or qualities of physicians themselves that will bear most directly on the achievements of their future careers? Intellectual capacity comes immediately to mind. Medicine is an extensive field, changing rapidly and dealing with a complex and stubborn organism. Intellectual capacity is important in doctors, and educational opportunity is not a substitute for native ability. I remind you of the motto of the University of Salamanca, which has been translated by the following couplet:

> *What nature hath denied,*
> *This University cannot provide.*

This is to say that education can develop only capabilities that are already there, and emphasizes the responsibility placed on medical schools to select students of a high level of intelligence.

However, as one observes doctors over decades, one comes to realize that some of the major diversities in the careers of physicians are to be found not in differences in intellect, but in differences in character — a matter much more difficult to describe and more subtle to measure. Instructive lessons may be learned by considering some of the factors that are associated with success on the one hand and with failure or partial performance on the other. Good performances in medicine are usually associated with good minds. They are almost invariably associated with certain aspects of personal quality. These include such matters as fortitude, stamina, vigilance, the capacity for sustained effort, the ability to accept responsibility; generosity, fairmindedness, integrity; and an imaginative capacity for seeing other people's problems. There is also the important matter of the habit of effectiveness. This habit is built on many aspects of character, including the capacity to finish matters that have been begun, the capacity to see long-term as well as immediate problems, and the capacity to deal effectively with people.

At this stage in any discussion of medical education and character, the question is raised whether anything can be done about one's character. My answer is that much can be done about it by people of intelligence, maturity, and perceptiveness who are willing to appraise themselves critically. One of the chief pleasures of my life as a teacher of medicine has been the opportunity to observe in medical students and young physicians the growth of effectiveness, the gradual substitution of order for confusion, and of accomplishment for good intentions, which indicate an evolution of character. I am now convinced that by taking thought one can add to one's moral and intellectual stature.

All physicians, if they are at all historically minded, are conscious of the tremendous technical advances in medicine in recent years, and are aware that physicians of today have an increased capacity to alter physiologic processes and so to control the evolution of disease and disability. In these very technical advances, and in the division of the profession into groups of experts, there is, however, a danger. The danger is that our intense desire to perform our technical duty effectively will lead us to neglect an aspect of medicine that has been part of our job since the days of Hippocrates' shadowy ancestors. This is the care of the patient as an individual, an aspect of medical care that is the obligation of every physician doing every type of technical medicine. Understanding, reassurance, and education are requirements of every patient who is ill.

The double task of the profession has been impressively set forth by Dr. Dana W. Atchley in an article in the *Saturday Review* entitled "The Healer and the Scientist"(1). He says: "An attempt to explore the essential forces that have caused the great changes in medicine over the past forty years leads our attention to two main categories of influence. There is, on one hand, the general increase of knowledge and, on the other hand, the evolution of the physician himself, his understanding, his wisdom, his philosophy." In another paragraph, he continues: "It is thus apparent that the physician of today, at his best, represents a fusion of the healer and the scientist. In his role he analyzes the multiple components presented by a single human being. As healer his intuitive understanding of the personality and environment is amplified by modern psychology; and scientific studies of the many facets of the structure and function of the physical machine inform him as to the existing organic status. The appraisal resulting from an integration of these data leads naturally to the special management appropriate to the particular individual. The introduction of the highest possible standards of scientific precision into clinical medicine is no deterrent to the exhibition of compassion or any of the other generous gifts of the healer. Merging the healer and the scientist combines the best capacities of both and loses nothing by the union." Such a merger of scientist and healer should be the object of medical education, including that essential portion that goes on throughout professional life.

At a time when medicine has so much to offer patients, it is a tragedy of the first order when its effectiveness is interfered with by defects of character or by bad manners. The role that manners play in the practice of medicine is a large one. Effective contact with patients and their families is largely a matter of good manners, which demonstrate the physician's concern for his patient and his effort to understand him. Counter demonstrations of rudeness, lack of consideration, or an obvious desire not to understand are guaranteed deterrents to effective practice. Good manners are a firm foundation of effective communication between doctor and patient. They can also be a firm foundation for effective understanding among doctors. Integrity of purpose and good manners will together solve most of the problems in medical ethics. When personal integrity, basic good manners, and a professional sense of discretion are combined, a good many problems of professional etiquette will solve themselves. Such matters as the physician's relation to the press, for example, are better dealt with by this combination of qualities than by specific rules.

Formal codes of medical ethics have existed for centuries. These codes are directed chiefly to the attainment of high standards of technical proficiency and of ethical behavior. The professional attitude of substituting the idea of service for that of gain is clearly set forth.

The best known and one of the noblest summaries is the so-called Hippocratic Oath, now some twenty-five hundred years old. The following translation is one of many. It is quoted from the handbook of Alpha Omega Alpha, an honor society in medical schools:

> I swear by Apollo, the physician, and Aesculapius, and Health, and Allheal, and all the gods and goddesses, that, according to my ability and judgment, I will keep this oath and stipulation: to reckon him who taught me this art equally dear to me as my parents, to share my substance with him and relieve his necessities if required; to regard his offspring as on the same footing with my own brothers, and to teach them this art if they should wish to learn it, without fee or stipulation, and that by precept, lecture and every other mode of instruction, I will impart a knowledge of the art to my own sons and to those of my teachers, and to disciples bound by a stipulation and oath, according to the law of medicine, but to none others. I will follow that method of treatment which, according to my ability and judgment, I consider for the benefit of my patients and abstain from whatever is deleterious and mischievous. I will give no deadly medicine to anyone if asked, nor suggest any such counsel; furthermore, I will not give to a woman any instrument to produce abortion. With purity and with holiness I will pass my life and practice my art. I will not cut a person who is suffering with a stone, but will leave this to be done by practitioners of this work. Into whatever houses I enter I will go into them for the benefit of the sick and will abstain from every voluntary act of mischief and corruption; and further from the seduction of fe-

males or males, bond or free. Whatever, in connection with my
professional practice, or not in connection with it, I may see or
hear in the lives of men which ought not to be spoken abroad,
I will not divulge, as reckoning that all such should be kept
secret. While I continue to keep this oath unviolated, may it be
granted to me to enjoy life and the practice of the art, respected
by all men at all times; but should I trespass and violate this oath,
may the reverse be my lot.

Dean Willard Sperry in his admirable volume *The Ethical
Basis of Medical Practice* (2) quotes a slightly different version.
He has this to say in comment: "In the main . . . the Oath is
forthright and intelligible. Apart from its dominant tone of warm
humanity and its concern for unselfish service, its details have
become mental second nature with all doctors. This is notably
so, for instance, in the insistence upon the inviolability of professional secrets. I know of no other profession which is as habitually
close-mouthed as that of medicine." Let me add the following:
If the general objectives of this noble directive are understood
and followed, the doctor can usually see clearly where his duty
lies.

We have mentioned the possibility that the spread of recent advances in medicine may lead doctors to forget or minimize the
patient as a person. There is another danger in the technical
advances of recent decades that also should be considered. Medical men deal with the human organism, whether they deal with
individuals or with groups. The rapid growth of knowledge
sometimes makes medical men forget that this organism with
which they work is an experienced one, which without the aid of
modern medicine has survived innumerable hazards, and biologi-
cally speaking has occupied the earth. This means to me that we
have an ally in our management of disease in the capacity of the
organism to adapt itself, shrewdly and successfully, to many of
the circumstances of disease. Hippocrates spoke of the *vis med-
icatrix naturae* and knew how to utilize it.

Dr. Jacob Bigelow in 1835 read to the Massachusetts Medical Society an article entitled "A Discourse on Self-limited diseases" (3). During a therapeutic era in which overtreatment is not unknown, it is perhaps worth while to recall some portions of his sagacious and imaginative statement: ". . . we may suspect those complaints to be self-limited, in which it is observed that the unwary, and the sceptical, who neglect to resort to remedies, recover their health without them. We may also suspect diseases to be of this character, when we find opposite modes of treatment recommended, and their success vouched for, by practitioners of authority and veracity . . ." Dr. Bigelow further pointed out that ". . . in many places, at the present day, a charm is popularly attached to what is called an active, bold, or heroic practice; and a corresponding reproach awaits the opposite course, which is cautious, palliative, and expectant . . ."; and that ". . . The longer and the more philosophically we contemplate this subject, the more obvious it will appear, that the physician is but the minister and servant of nature; that in cases like those which have been engaging our consideration, we can do little more than follow in the train of disease, and endeavor to aid nature in her salutary intentions, or to remove obstacles out of her path. . . ."

Physicians properly think of themselves as members of a profession. Let us give consideration to what is implied by this term. One definition of a profession is that it is a body of learned men whose primary responsibility is to serve the community and the individuals that compose it. The objective is not financial success, but effective performance in the professional field. There is nothing inconsistent in earning one's living by the practice of a profession, but this is not the first object nor the matter that controls either the attitude or the performance. If medicine is to maintain its standing, it is in the highest degree necessary that it should be composed of individuals who are driven not by acquisitiveness, but by interest, human understanding, and an intense and artistic desire to do perfectly the task before them. If medical men can attain this stature, so that their primary motivation is to play a beneficial role in the life of the world, and if they can maintain and improve their standards of scholarship, they can properly be called professionals. To be a professional it is necessary to be a scholar, a man of learning. It is necessary also to maintain and improve scholarship by continuing education. For this continuing education and his own continued growth, *the individual himself is responsible.*

Do not be confused about the location of this responsibility. It does not lie in specialty boards, in the chiefs of services, or in medical societies. All of these can be useful at the operative or tactical level; you yourself must be the strategist, the planner of the curriculum, and the executive officer.

Do not think that the types of medical careers are limited to the varieties that you see around you in your senior colleagues. Many new varieties of careers will be developed in this generation as they have been in all generations in the past, and you will develop them.

Finally, it is a general principle of teaching that a sound example is more effective than fine words. The relation of doctor and patient has many similarities to the relation of teacher and student. If you wish to convince your patients that they should lead well-ordered lives it will be well to provide a demonstration in your own life. You can hardly expect your precepts to be taken seriously unless you are prepared to exemplify them.

What has been said indicates that medicine is a laborious life of toil and discipline, with a grave, incessant responsibility for doing good work under all sorts of conditions. Therefore, no one should enter this profession or continue in it unless he is fundamentally interested in its subject matter. But if he is so interested, and if he accepts the toil, the discipline, and the responsibility, the rewards are there. They are the durable satisfactions of useful accomplishment, of overcoming difficulties, and of continuing growth.

There is no evidence that these durable satisfactions are available to any persons except those who earn them.

REFERENCES

1. ATCHLEY, DANA W. The Healer and the Scientist. *The Saturday Review,* January 9, 1954.
2. SPERRY, WILLARD L. *The Ethical Basis of Medical Practice.* New York: Hoeber, 1950, pp. 84, 85.
3. BIGELOW, JACOB. A Discourse on Self-limited Diseases Delivered before the Massachusetts Medical Society at Their Annual Meeting, May 27, 1835. Boston, 1835.

2

Family and Community Relations

by Henry F. Howe

THE PHYSICIAN AND HIS FAMILY

Most men and women who go into medicine do so for a combination of practical and idealistic reasons. It is an honorable profession. Despite its long period of training, it projects one promptly into respected community leadership. It provides an assured livelihood in a useful type of work. The physician has independence of judgment and of action. He lives by the use of his intellect and with intellectual honesty, beholden to no man, no political group, no industrial machine. He is free to raise his family in dignity in an atmosphere of social approval.

In return for these rewards he works harder than most men. As Dr. Howard A. Rusk and his Health Resources Advisory Committee reported, the average doctor in private practice up to the age of 45 works 60 hours a week. Not until the age of 65 does his work week fall below the accepted norm of 40 hours. Only one-third of physicians over 64 years of age are in retirement. Thus a physician packs into his working lifetime probably a third more working hours than the average man. These hours are inevitably subtracted from his leisure, his hobbies, his sleep, and his enjoyment of his family, and unless he plans with forethought, his family may make more of a sacrifice to his profession than is necessary.

Perhaps the most important measure of a man's personal success in a medical career is his degree of success in conducting his own family relations, for no career binds the private life of a man so closely with his working life as does the practice of medicine. The special devotion and dedication of the physician to his calling necessarily infringes upon the freedoms of his personal life. In a sense, indeed, he has no purely personal life, for the community demands a share in it at almost every point. Not only is his own leisure repeatedly interrupted by the telephone and the demands of his patients, reasonable or unreasonable, but his wife and children are inevitably forced to some extent into the mold of the life's work that he has chosen.

The problem begins in medical school. Marriage is often delayed. Interns and hospital residents live largely institutional lives even if married. Relative to their own generation they usually have children late and are older parents than the average. Their children are growing up amid the urgent complexities of the building of a practice. Their children's playtime and vacations are not infrequently interfered with by the peculiar emergencies inevitable in their father's life. All members of the family are necessarily drawn into the special relation that the doctor bears to the community, and a special type of household results. The home becomes an adjunct, to some degree, of the medical practice.

The wife has by her marriage accepted the problems of a medical career, with all its restrictions. If she is a nurse, she sometimes participates in the office routine. But the children have not chosen this career, and they sometimes suffer if the weariness, brusqueness, or irritability of the busy doctor are visited on them. They are not prepared to understand, so it is an obligation on their father to schedule for himself frequent participation in their playtime, enter into their games and projects, and closely follow their triumphs and achievements in school and juvenile organizations. He should know their teachers and playmates. He should give as much time as any other man to the business of being a good father.

The conscientious physician is thus beset with conflicting loyalties. As a younger man he usually deliberately works on week ends to build his practice. As an older man, busier through the week, he finds it is practically a lifesaving procedure for him to take definite time off call at regular intervals, for it is no part of the ethics of the profession to be a negligent father and die young of overwork.

Not only in the matter of vacations and weekends does the physician's allocation of his time and energy affect the welfare of his family. In recent years the financial squeeze of income taxes and increasing costs of labor supply have placed an economic dilemma before doctors in relation to the cost of salaried employees both in their offices and in their households. If to save money a doctor limits either his office or his household help below a minimum essential to care for his practice and his family needs, the added work load of nonmedical functions inevitably falls on himself and his wife. In the early years or in a small practice it may be necessary for clerical work and bookkeeping, odd jobs, and house cleaning to be shared in part at least by the husband and wife. But as a practice grows it may be a mistake for either the physician or his wife to use their fair share of what should be recreational time for this purpose. No formula can be laid down to determine what proportion of a doctor's gross income should be paid in salaries to employees, but in each individual situation an optimum proportion can be arrived at sufficient to allow the family to live properly.

The use and allocation of money have a great deal to do with the happiness of a family. This is particularly true in a professional career, where fee-for-service income is the chief source of livelihood. Earned dollars represent hours of hard work, and few physicians ever become really wealthy. It follows that expenditures must be proportioned to the amount of gainful work done. There is therefore no arbitrary living standard for a doctor except that he must live within his means, like other people. There are as many living standards of physicians as there are income levels. Yet there are many pressures on physicians urging them to keep up appearances. An attractive office, a decent car, and a pleasant home are the hallmarks of the profession. They are part of the stock in trade. An expensively dressed wife and memberships in the right clubs, expensive schools for the children, and a better car seem to some doctors as also stock in trade. Here we may part company. The latter items are luxuries, desirable to those who wish them, but not essential. Few people in these days value their doctor any more highly because of a display of wealth. Depressions and wars and taxes hit all alike, and if a physician begins to demonstrate symptoms of unwarranted opulence, the people are usually shrewd enough to suspect that he prizes the tangible returns from his practice more than service to the community or to his patients.

The physicians in a community are favorite subjects of gossip by every idle tongue. Doctors live in a goldfish bowl through whose magnifying qualities their smallest foibles are projected to the public eye. Greed, gluttony, drunkenness, and all the rest of the calendar of sins are manufactured by rumor out of the smallest of these foibles. Not the doctor alone suffers from these whispering campaigns, for his wife and children live under the same burden. They must adhere carefully to the same code of respectability that applies to his public character, or suffer the pain of hurting his career.

The physician moves across all social lines in the community and has friends in all groups. A few intimates have the run of the house, of course. But neither family loyalties nor social ambition can be allowed to interfere with the job, nor with the doctor's accessibility to the confidence of all kinds of people. He and his wife, by the nature of their calling, take part in civic

affairs and are looked up to for their public spirit. Their opinions
are sought on many community problems. Theirs is often a
special kind of household through which move many of the
projects for community improvement, many committees and
planning sessions for civic campaigns. All this is a part of their
professional function.

So in countless ways the physician's family lives somewhat
differently from others and frequently at a pace and in a turmoil
that few 40-hour-a-week working people would tolerate. The
wife sustains limitations on her freedom that make of her an
administrative head not only of a household, but also of a service center. The children are sometimes subjected to denials and
changes of some of their cherished projects, and occasionally are
made to feel that their father and mother are both too busy to
pay much attention to them.

But the family participates in the compensations of medicine
also. Neither the doctor nor his wife can be long unaware of
the enormous human satisfactions of their peculiar mode of living. For once in a while one sees a look in a human being's
face that, without words, speaks of a lifetime of grateful appreciation of a job well done. Oftener there is the lift the doctor
gets from a feeling of quiet trust and wholehearted confidence,
as when a mother has found sure haven for her child in his
care and some potential catastrophe has been averted. A wife
experiences a pride in her husband's successes that is quite im-
measurable in dollars, prestige, or social advancement. Even the
children get a vicarious satisfaction from seeing their father's
plaster cast on a friend's broken arm. They get to know that
their father is supposed to be a pretty smart man. The feeling
of belonging to the community, that the family is pulling its
weight in the boat, is a good one in which all the family shares.
Not only is a reasonable living assured, but there is respect, a
feeling of being wanted, and a whole circle of people who feel
grateful or dependent, or in some way show faith in one's in-

tegrity. These are the true rewards of medical practice everywhere. The sum of their treasure is measureless.

Also, there are dull seasons in any practice. During these weeks the physician has more freedom than the average businessman to pursue hobbies and enjoy his family. He has the advantage, being self-employed, of setting his own schedule for the elective cases, and may during such brief periods of light work enjoy a considerable measure of freedom. His vacations are his own to arrange, and if he can manage to combine them with time off for his family, they may count these trips and sojourns as the happiest times of their lives. They provide opportunity for periodic and most welcome breaks in the grind of household and career.

THE PHYSICIAN IN THE COMMUNITY

It has been hinted above that the somewhat monastic character of medical training sometimes prevents the younger physician from fully appreciating the social factors with which he will have to deal as a practicing physician in the community at large. The reason for this is that his training acquaints him only with a highly organized group of institutions, hospitals, schools, and charitable foundations, all working at a high pitch of efficiency to care for the health needs of the particular hospital segment of the public that is used as teaching material. The intern or resident sees a peculiarly regimented and standardized version of the community. Only when he emerges into individual practice does he become exposed to the same problems as they arise in the home or on the job, in the random and uncontrolled environment of community neighborhoods. In the hospital, all eyes and minds are directed in an orderly attack on the study and care of illness. In the open community, health interests must compete with a welter of business, social, and political pursuits that force the physician to choose how he shall limit and sched-

ule both his patients' lives and his own. Willy-nilly, he now himself becomes part of a neighborhood, and by his own way of
life to some extent determines the character of that neighborhood. In school and hospital his life was simple and direct. Now
quite suddenly he faces a community that is whimsical, often
bigoted and unreasonable, and full of prejudices and customs
that make good medicine hard to practice. There are employers
who fail to co-operate with their workmen's convalescent regimes,
people too ignorant to follow directions, working mothers unable to care for their children, and practical nurses with no training. There are glaring inadequacies in community health management. Such obstacles disturb the practitioner in his first
years and may turn him into either a crusader or a disgruntled
critic. The extremes of either tendency may do his practice much
harm. He has to learn that his patients come to him voluntarily
and take only what they are willing to take!

So he turns to the leading citizens of the community to see
what can be done. He is first of all himself a citizen of his
community, and like all citizens he can use its institutions as
tools for the study and possible amelioration of poor conditions.
He finds a number of types of organized effort that in one
way or another are related to the medical profession. Some are
government agencies; some are endowed or voluntarily administered. He will inevitably have official dealings with certain
of the municipal departments: the board of health, the board of
public welfare, perhaps the school committee, certainly the police
department, the courts, and the medical examiner. If he is wise,
he will early make himself familiar with the available facilities
of the state department of health, the Veterans' Administration,
tuberculosis and cancer clinics and hospitals, and such other government agencies as may help him. Whether he will some day
run for election to the board of health or school committee or
be school physician or accept appointment to an office under one
of the other agencies may be questions for eventual considera-

tion. Physicians have frequently served their communities well in public service, not only in the field of public health, but on advisory boards, committees, and even occasionally in state legislatures or in Congress. There is no barrier that automatically sets the physician apart as a special type of citizen who must abjure public office. He is by virtue of his learned profession a potential leader in the community; his advanced training and capacity for wise counsel may at times be turned to community use as justly as that of the lawyer, the banker, the professor, or the industrialist. His education prepares him better than most citizens for the planning of schools, municipal hospitals, and sanitary systems, and he may be called upon to serve on building committees or planning boards for the development of such public works as water systems, sewage plants, or health centers. He should accept his fair share of such responsibilities for the good of his community.

But in his early years of practice he is more likely to place his spare-time energies among the voluntary associations that are so characteristic and constructive a part of the American community. He will of course take active part in his hospital staff activities, and accept whatever committee work or charity services may fall to his lot. He should do the same for his district medical society, which is the best forum for his particular professional problems. Only at this level can he begin to hear and talk over effectively current problems that concern his professional life and future in state and national affairs, for the district medical society is a two-way street; information and opinions pass up and down it between the local profession and the larger medical associations. Particularly if a physician serves on an active committee of the district medical society he will find its liaison connections with state committees a stimulating experience in the processes of medical policy making.

Within the community there are many voluntary agencies that are nonmedical. Some of these such as the Red Cross, visiting nursing associations, community centers, the Young Men's Christian Association, and boy and girl scout organizations have a charitable interest collateral to medicine. These and the physician's religious affiliations normally demand support and good works proportional to the need and his capacity to serve. It is a wise thing for him to take an active part in some one or more of these excellent projects during the early years before his practice becomes too demanding on his time. It is unwise for him to take too many responsibilities in too many directions in such matters, however, for the tightly scheduled committee meetings night after night of even three or four such organizations can become an intolerable burden to himself and his family.

The same principle applies to the cultural and social activities of the community. If a physician takes a special delight in a community club or society of this sort, or if he is an ardent sculptor or photographer, one evening a week devoted to this as his hobby is a refreshing and rewarding experience. But the man who attempts to keep many such balls in the air at once over a period of years is risking an anxiety state or a hypertensive crisis. It may be well for the physician beginning practice to sample a fair number of such enterprises at various times during his career, but he should schedule his extracurricular time well within his capacity for enjoyment. These activities should be fun, not a heavy burden. For the physician is called upon for night work and long hours in his professional life, and should not be imposed on by community demands in the same volume as the person who works a 40-hour week.

One way of meeting this problem is to take only such responsibilities as are commensurate with his special talents. A physician might decline being a solicitor in a door-to-door financial campaign for a charity. But the same physician might logically serve on an advisory committee where his special knowledge would be valuable. A man is often happier if his community service makes use of special skills in which he is pre-eminent. He can frequently enjoy such service to the full, work hard at it, and not suffer the weariness and nervous tension that a routine job outside his own particular abilities produces. The demands on the practicing physician are multifarious in any case; he should deliberately choose for his extracurricular services the tasks he most enjoys. He can often thus combine to some degree his recreation and his community service time.

There are men to whom the practice of medicine is their whole life, or who have no talents aside from those of the diagnosis and treatment of disease. Some very fine physicians may be of this sort. But the classical picture of the revered physician, whether he is a family doctor of the old school or a noted specialist, is that of a broad-gauge man. He treats the whole patient, not merely a disease. He is as much interested in his patient's home, work, and neighborhood activities as he is in the illness of the moment.

The richer the doctor's store of familiarity with the neighborhood, the better doctor he is. How does one acquire that store of familiarity? By visiting homes, yes, in part. But if the doctor happened to have sat in a committee meeting one night with the patient's employer, his pastor, or his school principal, he may have learned certain factors in the patient's situation that he could not have learned in the home. Charity that begins at home can be continued and broadened by exchanges among skilled minds outside as well as inside the medical profession. If a doctor sits in counsel with community leaders for any reason at all, he is a better doctor for it.

There is also another factor. The kind of community one lives in is largely determined by the kind of voluntary leadership its organizations get. Who starts the scholarship funds by which certain poor boys eventually get to study medicine? Who sets in motion the campaigns for community hospitals? Who makes the medical plans for disaster or civil defense? The special interests and concerns of physicians should be represented in the planning of such projects, not only for the good of the community, but just as importantly for the good of the medical profession. A general refusal of doctors to give their time to community planning can only leave a vacuum of poor planning which eventually boomerangs on the doctors themselves. It is for lack of such doctor participation in community affairs that poor community health conditions become tolerated. The doctors, through constant community liaison with public officials, manufacturers, and health education groups, can educate these leaders to principles of preventive medicine that will make the community a good one in which to live.

There are other community activities that physicians frequently enter that have nothing to do with medicine. A physician, through investment or other circumstances, sometimes finds himself running a business, serving on boards of directors of banks or business enterprises, or developing real estate. Sometimes these activities may become a second career. To a certain degree they may work in perfectly well with the practice of medicine, but eventually they are likely to injure the practice or be so competitive for a man's time that he becomes a poor physician. No physician should delude himself that the pursuit of profit can mix well with the service motive of the medical profession. Whenever the desire for profit becomes dominant, a man would better abandon the practice of medicine and devote himself frankly to business.

3

The Doctor's Wife

by Kathryn L. McCabe

MARRIAGE AS A CAREER is usually considered the precious concern of only one member of the partnership — the wife. Women's magazines abound with advice concerning the career
aspects of matrimony, whereas publications catering to masculine
tastes seldom print articles in this vein. Obviously there can be
no hard and fast rules for successful marriage, but the current
quantity and variety of counseling indicates a widespread quest
for guidance. Matrimony appears to be a difficult business.

If marriage is always a demanding career, the medical profession makes special demands upon it. Physicians have more diversified careers than members of some other professions, but
by and large they are considered by the laity to be a homogeneous
group — all are doctors. Devoted to the specialties, to general
practice or internal medicine, surgery, public health, or pure research, the members of the medical profession encounter varying
problems in each husband-wife partnership. Just as the individual physician needs specialized training for his chosen field, so
must his wife develop particular skills in making their marriage
compatible. She must be executive, homemaker, diplomat, social
secretary, educator, and sundry other types of expert.

Much that can be said about the qualifications of the doctor's
wife applies, of course, to wives in general. Any stable lifelong
union requires love, good judgment, discernment, tolerance, pa-

tience and good humor. There are certain qualifications, however, that the doctor's wife requires in greater than usual degree,
and frequently she brings to her marriage advantages that help
her to cope with its special demands. She may be a person with
professional training who has had exacting contacts with people.
She sometimes has had a better education than other women
entering matrimony, and she is likely to have the advantage of
maturity, inasmuch as a doctor's training, lengthy and confining
as it is, tends to discourage early marriage — although it is true
that the tendency to marry early is on the increase.

Since a doctor's wife is undertaking a challenging career, she
needs to cultivate certain habits as implements for success — good
habits of thought and behavior in relation to people, the understanding of human problems, discretion and restraint in conduct,
good taste in personal grooming, and orderliness in her environment. Essential to the establishment of these good habits is the
ability to plan efficiently. As a physician's partner, not only does
a woman have to schedule ordinary household routine, but she
must also provide for the added demands of a busy telephone and
special social and civic obligations. Timetables, however, are not
the answer to everything. A physician's wife soon realizes that
a well-scheduled life can be planned, but it can seldom be carried
out to the letter. The exigencies of her situation, therefore, demand elasticity in her planning. There must always be provision
for free time to cope with frequent disruptions, and allowance
for breathing spells to collect thoughts and person for better and
more gracious living.

It might truthfully be said that a doctor's wife lives public relations. She enjoys a unique position in the community, a position that she assumes in part with matrimony but keeps by her
own efforts. The physician's esteem in the community may be
increased by his wife when she sincerely and diligently tries to
further his professional interests. However, thoughtless acts by

the wife of any citizen can damage the prestige held by her husband. Although she shares in some measure the esteem felt for
her husband, by and large she has to earn regard for herself in
her own right. As with all public figures, a foolish act can make
the best of intentions a matter for venomous castigation.

A most important field of public relations includes organizations and affiliations. The word to the wise is to be a cautious
joiner. Although a doctor's wife may be tempted to accept membership in all the organizations in the community to avoid appearing to discriminate, she may be criticized for having too
many or too frivolous affiliations. From her own standpoint,
membership in too many organizations wastes time and money,
dilutes the effectiveness of work in enterprises really worth while,
and gives the unfavorable impression of publicity seeking. It is
impossible to present a yardstick for measuring the worth of
groups. A simple but effectual gauge is evaluation of the amount
and type of service they give. However, the wife of a physician
must consider her husband's position before joining certain
groups. Those organizations offering her an opportunity to use
her own knowledge and the resources to which she has access for
furthering health and welfare within the community are usually
deserving. From the standpoint of family teamwork, she may
develop an interest in groups that give her a chance to learn more
about her husband's field and how to function within it. Such
an organization is the Woman's Auxiliary to the American Medical Association. Now coming into its own, the Auxiliary offers
education and channels information about the medical profession,
its organization and its projects, medical economics, legislation,
public health, and welfare problems. Women's clubs, the Junior
League, the Red Cross, and civic and cultural clubs also afford
valuable outlets.

Money-raising ventures should be approached with caution.
There seems to be a certain sensitivity concerning the doctor's

financial status. His yearly income and its expenditure are unfairly compared with the earnings and expenses of an unskilled or semiskilled worker employed 40 hours a week. The time involved in preparing for the medical profession and the long hours spent in earning a livelihood are frequently overlooked or forgotten. When a doctor's wife engages in an enterprise, therefore, she should remember that, although she is acting on her own, she implicates her husband; in lending her name she is also lending her husband's sacred possession. She should know for what organization and purpose her name is being used and what she is sponsoring. With care, she can avoid embarrassment to her husband and his profession as well as to herself.

Closely allied to public relations is the matter of publicity. Pictures or signed articles in newspapers or periodicals may be intended to represent only the individual named, but they are often interpreted as representing the profession, despite the fact that the one mentioned is the wife of a member rather than a member. Likewise, the spoken word should be carefully handled. Too often the doctor's wife's casual comment is repeated out of context as an authoritative statement, so that it becomes distorted and implausible. Habits of discretion and restraint need to be so inculcated that silence, tactful evasion, or feigned ignorance is the automatic reaction when direct response would involve divulgence of confidences. Ignorance sometimes has greater rewards than mere bliss.

One of the assets of being a doctor's wife lies in the excellent opportunities for friendships. Upon her entrance into a community, many doors are thrown open. However, friendships are reciprocal; none are made except by the attraction of minds and hearts. Gossip, tactless remarks, and inconsiderate behavior are deterrents.

Good habits in the field of human relations are constantly put to the test by the telephone. This device is in many ways a diabolical invention and a disturber of the happiness of doctors'

homes. Nonetheless, it is a most essential piece of equipment —
one of the instruments by which the physician makes his services
available to the community. It is a mechanical barrier to the
advantages of personal appearance — a barrier that can be overcome, however, by the development of a pleasant telephone personality and a genuine interest in the problems of the person at
the other end of the wire. The telephone is also often a buffer
between the physician and personal intrusions.

Not to mention the doctor's wife in connection with his office
would be to neglect an association that can be valuable in maintaining good public relations, but that may easily give rise to
awkward domestic relations. Particularly in urban areas, the
separation of home and office is becoming customary, and it is
desirable if at all feasible. When the house must also shelter an
office, however, some thought and effort are required to retain
the atmosphere of a home. A room can hardly be described by the
adjective "living" when it must accommodate waiting patients.
For the family's peace of mind and a wholesome degree of normal
life, an office in the home should be made as distinct from the
living quarters as possible.

In the early stages of practice or in particular localities, it is
sometimes a matter of necessity for a wife to function as an office
assistant. Such an arrangement requires a high degree of tact
and adaptability to be entirely successful. In situations where
the office is apart from the home and assistance is employed, the
doctor's wife needs to exercise restraint and consideration also.
Although she appreciates his office help as her ally in making her
husband's life easier and more efficient, she must refrain from
intimacy and interference. The areas in which the doctor's wife
and his office assistant function must be delineated. Personal
shopping, errands, and secretarial work for the doctor's wife are
outside the province of office duties.

In a sense the nuptial ceremony does not denote a *fait accompli*.
Rather it is the debut to a rewarding life. Usually a physician

marries when he is starting his professional career. Concomitant
with success, he will grow within his profession and within his
community. His wife must keep pace and not be the girl he
left behind him. Therefore a program of self-improvement and
education must provide resources to help combat the tendency of
the medical profession to become culturally stagnant. The twen-
tieth-century doctor, busy caring for his patients, attending meetings, reading medical journals, and working in professional and
civic organizations, is apt to find little time to devote to outside
interests other than a few social affairs. It falls to his wife to
bring into the household something of the cultural advantages of
the community, and to have stimulation and diversion in this
vein to offer him when he comes home at night, weary with the
aches, pains, and illnesses of his patients or the insoluble problems of his work. A doctor may not have time to visit the art
gallery, read books and current periodicals, or attend the theater
but at least he can know something of them. He may develop
an interest in hobbies, the antidote to worry and tension, when
he has someone to foster and share his interest.

From a selfish but no less worthy standpoint, a program of
self-improvement and expanding interests helps fill the vacuum
created for some wives by being too often and too long alone.
The physician is so frequently away from home that his wife
either has to create her own diversion or be mired in a rut. Existence in a rut is straightforward — straight down the road to
boredom. Outside activities such as academic courses, postgraduate study in the field forsaken for marriage, or lessons to
develop an engrossing hobby dispel the aura of self-pity with
which some women become surrounded.

No one needs to cultivate good health habits more than the
physician's wife. Not only does she need good health for her
vigorous type of living, but close as she is to medical care, she
remains on the outer fringes as a recipient. During the upheaval
about national health insurance when many words were used to

describe the medically indigent, it was frequently jested with a grain of truth that doctors' families comprised the medically indigent. Seeking home as a haven free from ills, the doctor may not see the trees for the woods. His family is too close to be observed objectively. At home, illness is not expected. A complaining wife with a daily catalogue of aches and pains to report may bar herself from careful medical consideration at the home source.

Guided by wisdom and ethical code, a physician does not usually treat his own family. The doctor's family needs a family doctor other than the doctor in the family. Furthermore, one doctor treats another doctor and his family without fee. Under the circumstances, it is readily seen that embarrassment, fear of imposing, or reluctance to consult for what may be an imagined ailment becomes magnified for this group. Doctors advocate annual or semiannual physical checkups for the general public, but their families do not usually subscribe. Many doctors' families, particularly those with several children, join voluntary health insurance plans beyond hospitalization so that, other than house calls and the too rare office visits, impersonal compensation can be made to the attending physician without embarrassment; this procedure is somewhat frowned upon, however. Without the provision of some type of insurance, there arises the matter of a token gift in lieu of compensation. Here looms the bugbear in the field of courtesy. How much of a gift and what type of gift? Doctors' houses are loaded with unique items carefully selected by grateful colleagues which stand collecting dust. No physician ever begrudges the time and talent given gratuitously in the care of another physician's family illness. The occasional doctor's wife who bestows her every vague pain on the specialist in the field in which she believes her pain arose deserves the criticism she receives.

The problem of managing an illness of the head of the family is too idiosyncratic for more than general comment. Doctors suc-

cumb to illness in two ways: either by completely ignoring it in re-
signed silence while awaiting the Maker's call, or by the self-diag-
nosis and self-treatment method in the face of assumed dire
prognosis. Both instances are terrifying household experiences
that can be handled successfully only by a woman with the
qualities of a supreme court justice, the authority of an army
sergeant, and the patience of Job.

Despite the foregoing admonitions and expositions concerning
various types of relations, professional, community, social, and
public, it is well to remember that matrimony is undertaken
primarily for the development and maintenance of a particular
sphere of relations — family relations. Every woman expects the
man of her choice to have some special attributes, a few minor
vices, an attractive number of virtues, and a varying number of
relatives. The physician's wife should expect as an added dividend a goodly portion of the community with whom she must
share her husband. Early in marriage, a sensible wife is aware
that she is often secondary to her husband's work. Young physicians in turn need to realize early that unintentional or unavoid-
able neglect, unlike the "scientific neglect" sometimes prescribed
for patients, never proves beneficial as sustained treatment in a
case of matrimony.

Few women are left as completely in charge of their families
as is the mistress of the doctor's household. The mother of a
doctor's children serves in a dual capacity. She is always mother;
she is often a substitute father. Late home-comings, sporadic
contacts with his children, and preoccupation with his professional responsibilities can place a father in a position of dis-
advantage, as the provider of the family income but the less
influential parent. Unless care is exercised, the children may become alienated from their father or hostile toward his profession.
Here the mother is really put to the test of underplaying her dual
role with such skill that the father is a member of the family
group although irregularly in evidence. Natural expression of

irritation concerning her husband's absence from home or his lateness at dinner or any emphasis on the mother's double responsibilities can develop in a child feelings of hostility toward his father. The children must understand that their father is missing from the family circle only because of his obligations. However, they should not feel that their family is unique, belonging in a special category. They should be taught that many families lead lives quite as disrupted. The importance of the doctor's contribution to man's welfare should be emphasized, and the inconvenience involved in making this contribution minimized.

A means of banishing feelings of separateness and strengthening a child's sense of security and "belonging" is the appearance, when possible, of both parents at school, parent-teacher, scout, or church functions. Recognizing the need for making many decisions and for accepting an unusual amount of parental responsibility, the doctor's wife needs to take care that she does not arrogate paternal authority in the management of her children. By careful evaluation, she can determine the matters in which she is competent to make decisions alone and recognize those better reserved for the consideration of both parents. A family responsibility that both mother and father must share is that of education. Schooling is not just the mother's decision nor does it fall within the category of trivia that the father should be spared. It is not a matter to be decided within minutes but to be planned according to the character of the child. Sometimes a physician may be disappointed to discover that a son or daughter has no inclination to follow in his footsteps. Awareness of the type and quality of education his children are receiving and knowledge of their inclinations and potentialities will assist him in understanding their needs and formulating definite plans for their future. The broad social experience to which children are now exposed may present vocations more attractive than the apparently preordained profession of medicine.

Doctors' children almost more than any others need to realize their obligations as citizens and members of an important family. The father brings home the news of various activities and of people in the community. It is all too easy to bring home also the malice and gossip concerning public personalities and civic affairs or drop an unguarded word about intimate affairs of patients. Early in life, children must be made aware of the meaning of responsibilities and confidences. The trust never to repeat conversations overheard or any sort of information concerning professional matters must become part of the child's fiber. Parents can mitigate the severity of this charge imposed at an early age by bearing in mind that members of the family cannot repeat what they haven't heard. How very fortunate is the doctor's family that has encountered no greater dereliction than an enterprising young son's sale of tickets for admission to his father's library to view illustrations in medical books! The doctor's and the clergyman's children share alike the pains of the halo that pinches.

One of the most important ingredients in the adhesive binding a physician's family together is shared recreation. Since she must plan family activities to a greater degree than most wives, the doctor's wife should make provisions for periods of relaxation to be enjoyed by the whole family. This frequently requires skillful and tactful maneuvering. Definite times for enjoying leisure together can be arranged, and whether the family vacation is a matter of one week or one month, annual or semiannual, it is often the only opportunity for the doctor's family to join together in play and relaxation away from the telephone and the exactions of practice. It is also a time when the father can assume his responsibility fully and reinforce his position within the family circle. Vacations and leisure offer concentrated periods for the growth of feelings of security. Family security is the foundation of any child's normal development, and doctors' children are no exception. Inexpensive or costly in terms of money, the family holiday reaps dividends only in proportion to the interest and attention expended.

A wise purchaser balances expenditures for any item against the worth of goods received. Many times, expenditures must be balanced against cost in public relations as well. In the matter of housing, too often the physical aspects of the structure are considered as typifying the sort of home life within. Gracious living does not depend on ostentatious trimmings, however, and orderliness frequently achieves better results than ornamentation. Usually the proper balance is determined and maintained by the lady of the household.

Family finances, a concern of all wives, are another area in which a doctor's wife may have unusual responsibilities. Many men have a stable income against which their wives can balance the outlay. Some physicians receive salaries, but rarely do these salaries represent the entire earned income. By and large, most physicians' incomes fluctuate. Therefore it is extremely difficult to budget on either a weekly or monthly basis. Along with budgeting time and activities, the business of apportioning the family income to meet the family needs rests with the doctor's wife. Sharing knowledge of her husband's practice, she can estimate within what bracket they should live. It is her duty to be bookkeeper for the household portion of the outlay of money. This involves not only anticipating and providing for the expenses of running her household, but helping her husband with those accounts in which office and home expenses must be co-ordinated for such purposes as income tax reports. It is her responsibility to keep receipted bills and canceled checks for the legitimate deductions. This is particularly true of household repairs and improvements, and contributions to charitable or educational organizations. Systematic bookkeeping may mean the difference between a higher or lower income tax bracket. A ledger or card index file system can be used to keep monthly records of those large routine expenditures, property taxes, mortgage payments, and insurance premiums that regularly fall due, as well as of income from investments which supplement professional earnings. By systematic accounting she can anticipate those months in which the family budget will be strained, and also foresee the months of lesser expenses when there will be an opportunity for investments or improvements.

Included in expenses is the cost of household help. The type of life she leads may often justify some form of household help for the doctor's wife, a matter that should be approached from the standpoint of need and income only, and not from that of appearances. With modern appliances so numerous and varied, it is well to consider whether the expenditure for modern automatic time-saving conveniences does not make life easier than an extra pair of hands within the house. Every pair of hired hands is accompanied by a mouth to feed and a disposition to cope with, not to mention social security taxes and adequate liability insurance. A poorly trained helper is worse than none, both economically and socially. Any maid must have thorough training in the matter of discretion. A little dirt left on dishes may cause intestinal distress and family inconvenience, but a little dirt spread in the community may cause professional embarrassment. No person within the doctor's household should answer the telephone or meet patients unless adequately trained to handle such contacts. Training is best given by precept, and many of the good habits formed by the doctor's wife need to be acquired by all those comprising the household.

With all the special qualifications and considerations required to be successful as the wife of a physician, how apt seem the words of Robert Browning:

> . . . Love, we are in God's hand.
> How strange now looks the life he makes us lead;
> So free we seem, so fettered fast we are!

However, the special demands are usually well met because of the character of the partners involved. Physicians are by inclination and training discerning men, wise in human relations and keen in judgment. It would seem logical that such men should make their lifelong alliance with partners of comparable astuteness and wisdom.

4

Choice of Opportunities

by James Howard Means

To THE YOUNG MAN or woman who has just earned the degree
of doctor of medicine, there unfolds a rich spectrum of opportunity. As some years earlier the choice of medicine as a career had
to be made, so now again a choice has to be made; this time that
of what area of medicine the young doctor shall enter. No longer
can any one person encompass it all. Some graduates may select
a relatively wide portion of the spectrum, others may focus
sharply on one of its narrower bands, but never should any of
them let the light of the whole fade entirely from the field of their
professional sensibility.

In making his choice the young doctor must have in his mind
some understanding of the over-all nature of medicine and of its
place and function in the total social order. Also he must practice some self-scrutiny in order to identify as best he can his own
motivations, interests, and skills. He must think in terms of what
variety of medical work he can do best and of what kind has the
most attraction for him. The greatest rewards of any professional
work lie in the satisfaction of doing it well and of extending the
boundaries of what it can accomplish. Medicine is, and should
be — for the good workman is worthy of his hire — a well-paid
profession, but let no one embrace it whose primary objective is
mercenary.

Broadly speaking, medicine nowadays can be said to be one

of the great sinews of the social organism. It has the function of promoting, preserving, and restoring the health both of persons and communities. In such a capacity it has in its hands the manpower of a nation. This total function can be subdivided in various ways. One way would be into the practice of medicine, medical education, and medical research. Practice in the traditional sense means care of the patient. Today, however, we hear the term "public health practice" used with increasing frequency — the routine work of the health officer. He seeks to do for the community what the practitioner of medicine does for individuals.

The main purpose of this book is to serve as a guide to the practice of medicine as it applies to the individual, but according to my own philosophy the practice of medicine in its broad aspects is inextricably bound up with education and research. Without research there is no progress, and without education there are no new doctors. Every doctor must always seek ways of imparting his skill and use his powers of observation to uncover new facts. Of recent years certain doctors of medicine have devoted themselves more exclusively to teaching and research than to practice, but if they are doctors of medicine they should engage to some extent in the care or problems of patients, because otherwise they will cease to be competent to teach medicine or to recognize the questions that medicine needs to have answered.

Coming now to those doctors primarily engaged in the practice of medicine, we are able to divide them, by the broad nature of their approach to the care of patients, into physicians, surgeons, and psychiatrists; or by what portion of the whole content of medicine they seek to cover, into specialists and generalists (the latter still commonly called general practitioners). The propriety of equating the role of the psychiatrist with the roles of the physician and surgeon will be challenged by many, but I submit that currently a good deal of evidence is accumulating to justify such an appraisal. William C. Menninger has well pointed out that the

anatomy of the personality is no less a concern of the doctor than
the anatomy of the body. That this concept is not entirely new is
witnessed by the fact that Robert Burton wrote in 1621 on *The
Anatomy of Melancholy*. Nevertheless Dr. Menninger is fully
justified in pointing out that our present-day medical profession
is insufficiently aware of it. Moreover, in dealing with the problems of the personality there is available now a wealth of new
knowledge undreamed of until the beginning of the work of
Freud only sixty years ago.

The young doctor of today at medical graduation time is con-
fronted merely with the choice of which of these general approaches to practice he will follow. Indeed, he need not make
even this choice until later, because before him lie one or often
several years of graduate training in hospital house staff jobs,
during which his inclination will be clarified. Certainly his choice
of a narrow clinical specialty may be deferred until well along
in the house staff training or even later.

The majority of internships offered by American hospitals at
present are of the mixed or rotating type. They encompass brief
bits of practical training in a variety of fields of medicine. A
single year of such experience is hardly adequate training even
for the most general of general practices. Yet it is all that a certain portion of medical graduates are getting in the United States
today. As a prelude to assistant residencies and residencies more
specialized in scope, however, the one-year rotating internship
often is quite satisfactory.

A minority of hospitals, but from the training point of view
among the best, require from the very start a choice between
medicine and surgery. They offer straight services in medicine on
the one hand, or in surgery on the other. The graduate who
chooses such a straight service has usually decided at least whether
he wishes to become a physician or a surgeon. There are exceptions, such as when having finished a straight medical internship
the graduate switches to surgery. This is a good program if he can

afford the time. I know of instances in which graduates of straight surgical internships even ended up as psychiatrists.

For the purpose of making a primary choice between medicine, surgery, and psychiatry, the individual must know something of the nature of these callings and what it takes to serve them. The traditional separation of members of the medical profession into subspecies is into physicians and surgeons. Psychiatrists, as such, came later. The contrast between physician and surgeon is exemplified by such terms as "College of Physicians," "College of Surgeons," or "College of Physicians and Surgeons." That two callings are involved is also implied by the signs of those doctors of medicine who proclaim to the public that they are both physician and surgeon. There is no difficulty about the term surgeon. He is one who treats the sick by means of the knife. His is a special approach and he himself is a specialist. The term physician, however, is more nebulous. In Dr. Johnson's famous dictionary (1755) we find: "Physician — One who professes the art of healing." This definition obviously includes the surgeon — the surgeon is a subspecies of physician. About two hundred years later we find in a modern dictionary of American English: "Physician, (a) one who practices the art of healing (obsolete) and (b) one legally qualified to practice medicine — often distinguished from a surgeon." It is in the latter sense that I like to use the term physician. I consider that that is what I am myself. It means that I have some competence for caring for the patient, but none at all for performing surgical operations or carrying out the special technics of a number of narrow specialties. There is justification for such a course even in the oath of Hippocrates, in which it is said: "I will not use the knife, not even verily on sufferers from stone, but I will give place to such as are craftsmen therein."

The personality traits and aptitudes that go toward making the good physician differ from those that are needed in the make-up of the good surgeon. The surgeon performs in the limelight. He is the virtuoso of medicine. His professional work consists to a considerable extent in dealing with crises. At least to the patient the surgical operation is a crisis. The surgeon enters, and often leaves, the patient's life at this time of crisis. The surgeon, in a sense, is always on the spot. He must make vital decisions with great rapidity. He must know his way around inside the human body with utter accuracy, certainty, and confidence. He must be a robust, resilient, psychologically extroverted sort of person. Had he not such qualities he could not take what the surgeon has to take.

The function of the physician is quite different. He is less concerned, at least if he is of the category that I have called generalist, with crises than with the sustained care of patients, keeping them well if he can, or trying to restore them to health if they become sick. He applies any sort of treatment that he is competent to give and calls in specialists when skills beyond his competence are indicated. The qualities required to make the good physician are understanding, insight, purposeful sympathy, responsibleness, and patience. His personality also must be one to inspire confidence. He is not on the spot as is the surgeon, and can more readily admit error without losing either face or patient, provided the patient has trust in him. His concern is with the whole individual. He is indeed the personal physician.

The specialist occupies an intermediate position between the physician and the surgeon, in the sense in which I have used these terms. Often he retains charge of patients for long periods, but he is taking care of only a part of them. The difference, as I see it, between the three categories of practitioners of medicine that I have mentioned is that the surgeon is interested primarily in the operation and the specialist in the disease, but the nonspecialized physician or generalist is interested primarily in the person.

Speaking of persons, I should like now, before outlining opportunities in the narrower clinical specialties, and nonclinical opportunities in medicine, to indicate the role and place of psychiatry in the medical spectrum of our times. Is psychiatry a specialty? Most people would say yes, of course, but I think it is not completely so. It is a specialty in that it uses specialized technics and requires rather long special training; but in its field of operation it is hardly a specialty, inasmuch as it deals with the whole height, depth and breadth of the human personality. Except for pediatrics and geriatrics, which are general medicine applied to an age group, the clinical specialties are focused on organs, diseases, or technics, not on persons. Psychiatry, on the other hand, is most assuredly focused on persons — on personalities, in fact. So much so that the psychiatrist, though nowadays always a doctor of medicine, may sometimes miss an organic process that is perhaps causing no symptoms, or erroneously interpret symptoms as of purely psychic origin that actually result from primary organic disease. The psychiatrist, being a graduate in medicine, is competent, by training, to examine the patient completely in body as well as mind, but usually he depends on the physician to take care of the former.

The objectives of psychiatry have broadened greatly in the last few decades, and to the medical graduate of today, psychiatry offers a wealth of opportunity for interesting professional work undreamed of at the turn of the century. Fifty years ago diagnosis in psychiatry amounted to not much more than the taxonomy of lunacy, and its therapeutics consisted of giving custodial care in a mental hospital or sanitarium. Today the situation has considerably improved. The modern psychiatrist's first objective is to keep people mentally well. To a great extent his has become largely an office instead of an institutional practice. The stigma of psychiatry is becoming dispelled from the minds of the people. Patients voluntarily seek the services of psychiatrists when faced with emotional problems they have difficulty in resolving. The discipline has shifted from a negative to a positive approach in the care of patients.

What it takes to make a good psychiatrist is similar to what is required for the nonspecialized physician. But certain traits must be more intensely cultivated. The ability to attain to very great objectivity and patience is paramount. Also there must be deep and genuine interest in people as persons, and in the dynamics of human relations. Intellectual capacity and general education sufficient to permit understanding and communication with highly intelligent people likewise are essential.

The psychiatrist's life can be more regularly ordered than that of most other practitioners. Except when he is called out to deal with an acutely psychotic patient, which of course can be a dizzy business, his work can be ordered and scheduled by the clock just as he pleases. By common consent, when the psychiatrist is with his patient he is incommunicado, whereas the ordinary doctor is expected to answer the telephone regardless of what he is doing.

Before coming to the true specialists let us also consider the so-called internist. Just what is he? To the laity the term is largely meaningless, or it may be confused with intern. Despite the fact that the root word in one case means inside the patient, and in the other inside a hospital, we find a recent standard American dictionary actually giving intern as synonymous with internist! In most general dictionaries the word internist cannot be found at all. Only in the medical dictionaries can one find it, and even then the definition is apt to be disconcerting. For example, "One who treats internal diseases; a physician distinguished from a surgeon"; but does not the surgeon treat internal diseases, and does not the internist sometimes treat external ones? Is the internist a specialist? To be sure there is a specialty board in internal medicine, but does that make him a specialist? Perhaps the best approach is to observe what he does, and having done that, it may appear that there is but little sense in calling him an internist. In actual practice one finds so-called internists engaged rather heavily in diagnostic work, much of it in consultation with general practitioners, or in treating patients with a wide variety of diseases, or passing them on to the narrower specialists when he cannot supply what they need himself. In fact, then, it seems to me that he is nothing more nor less than the nonspecialized physician that I have already defined, but with a specialist's rating. Personally I much prefer the term physician to that of internist, an exotic term imported some decades ago from Germany. I find, moreover, that our British medical colleagues share this feeling.

Of the narrower clinical specialties as career opportunities in medicine, certain general statements may be made. Knowing more and more of less and less is the now bromidic remark that is often made of them. It is very unseemly, however, to disparage them, for they are absolutely essential if all that medical science has to offer is to be made available to the patient. Difficult and special technics are often required in the specialties in either diagnosis or treatment. Many doctors find complete contentment in the practice of these specialties. They may become intellectually satisfying, particularly if, together with care of patients, there is included in the specialist's program some research and teaching.

All clinical specialties presuppose an adequate clinical training in general medicine, and many of them, for example ophthalmology, otolaryngology, urology, proctology, gynecology, obstetrics, and orthopedics, require a good grounding in general surgery as well. Such nonoperative specialties as neurology, dermatology, allergy, cardiology, endocrinology, gastroenterology, and radiology need only a preceding general medical experience. The recent graduate must first get his general clinical training and then embark on his training for a specialty. It is a lengthy progression, but a great many are eager to follow it. The older and well-established specialties all have their specialty certifying boards, which lay down certain minimum training requirements for certification, although there is no legal mandate that the specialist must receive his board certification before practicing his specialty. The weight of professional opinion is such that he will have tough going without it.

Besides the more formal and traditional specialties, there are cropping up all the time new ones that start off merely as special interests within a broader field. A general physician, or internist if you like, may develop an interest in some special clinical problem — a certain disease perhaps — and make himself an authority on it. He does not limit his practice to it, but if he gains a reputation in it he is consulted by other doctors who think he may have something special to contribute in certain of their cases. Thus many generalists will also be informal specialists in a field that has particular interest for them. And this is altogether desirable. The special interest is challenging and often seems to keep the generalist more alert to medical progress than he would be without it. General surgeons, too, often gain particular skill in some highly specialized procedure, but at the same time they would not want to confine their work to it, nor would it be desirable that they do so.

In making up his mind in what variety of medical practice he will engage, the doctor of today has many questions to consider, not only whether he will be generalist or specialist, but also in what sized community he will settle, and whether he will practice by himself or as a member of a practice group. Solo practice of medicine is the traditional pattern, but with the growing complexities of modern diagnosis and treatment, teamwork of some sort for the provision of medical care is becoming ever more important. Solo practitioners, generalists and specialists, can and do collaborate to provide complete medical care to patients, but medical care by such collaboration may be less effective and more costly to the patient than that which he could get from an organized practice group. A great variety of groups already exist in the United States today, and there is considerable evidence that many of the younger doctors are glad to join them. There is a good deal of satisfaction in being a member of a group, with the moral support that such teamwork affords, to say nothing of better hours of work and financial stability. Groups giving complete service, of course, must be composed of such proportions of generalists, to act as the patients' personal physicians, and appropriate specialists as will supply at least all the usual skills that comprehensive medical care requires.

As between generalist and specialist it can be said that the former has a richer experience in human relations; he knows and understands his patients better as persons, whereas the latter perhaps has greater intellectual satisfaction in gaining mastery of special technics and achieving scholarship in a defined field.

Choice of location — urban, suburban or rural — will be governed by the tastes of the doctor. The majority nowadays flock to the cities. There is great need, however, for doctors in the less thickly settled areas. A few rugged extroverts will accept the challenge of rural solo practice, but not in sufficient numbers to solve the rural medical care problem. It will take good community organization and planning of rural medical care programs to do that. A number of such enterprises have already been launched in various parts of the country, some as co-operatives, some on other bases. They are bound to increase in number and scope, and undoubtedly will offer to many younger physicians and surgeons new and interesting opportunities.

Let us next turn our attention to full-time academic opportunities for doctors of medicine. These, compared with private practice opportunities, are relatively few in number, but they are of great importance from the point of view of medical progress, and also their numbers are increasing because of both the increasing complexity of medical education and the greatly expanding medical research program of the nation.

A very small number of medical graduates may elect to forgo all thought of practice or of any sort of clinical work, and instead spend their professional lives in one of the preclinical sciences such as anatomy, physiology, biochemistry, microbiology, immunology, or pharmacology. For such careers the medical training is not wasted, but it is by no means imperative. There are distinguished professors of these subjects on faculties of medicine throughout the land who are not doctors of medicine. Pathology, on the other hand, is much more closely integrated with clinical practice, and those who elect careers in this field, although they may never have direct care of patients, need a medical training in order to interpret their findings correctly.

Academic positions in the clinical departments of our medical schools and their affiliated teaching hospitals, on the other hand, require the longest and most thorough training at the house staff level of any of the medical callings. Nowadays aspirants for such positions must work up through all the grades of residents in either medicine or surgery, and usually top them off with some years in clinical research before they finally get on the ladder of university advancement. To such people falls the major responsibility of determining and leading the course of medical education. They are concerned with the organization of teaching and of ever seeking to improve its character and quality. They have the duty of enriching the educational process by integrating it with the investigative. In the university medical center the three functions of medicine — practice, teaching, and research — are thoroughly blended, to the enhancement of each. The full-time clinical teachers are for the most part the guides, guardians, and activators of this process. To the scholarly-minded young doctor there are challenging opportunities here. Great happiness can be had in such careers, but the financial rewards are less than those that may be had in private practice.

A variation of this type of career is that of the full-time clinical investigator. This is the doctor who is not so concerned, if at all, with teaching, but elects to spend his time entirely in the investigation of disease, making use for this purpose of clinical cases. In contrast to the anatomist, physiologist, or biochemist, who conducts his investigations entirely in the laboratory and at the experimental level, the clinical investigator must know his medicine thoroughly, for the very reason that he makes use of patients in his studies and is responsible for their welfare. The opportunities for careers of this type are rapidly increasing both in the clinical departments of medical schools and in a variety of research institutes. The government in particular, since the last war, has inaugurated research programs in several of its departments. These all require increasing numbers of competent clinical investigators. Notable among these undertakings is the Clinical Center of the United States Public Health Service, a research hospital with 500-bed capacity at Bethesda, Maryland, opened in 1953. It will take a veritable army of investigators to make full use of such a volume of clinical material. Whether the divorcement from the formal medical educational process that this arrangement entails will, in the long run, prove altogether desirable remains to be seen. I have some doubts of it myself. The cross-fertilization of practice, education, and research will be impaired.

There are other important fields of endeavor open to the doctor of medicine. Public health work is one of the most significant and rapidly expanding of these. In medicine as it relates to the individual we have practice, teaching, and research; so too are all these functions intrinsic to the public health profession.

To enter the public health field the doctor of medicine upon graduation may enter a school of public health and spend one year for certification, or three for the doctorate in public health. Then he will probably perform his professional work on salary from the federal government, a state or local government, a university, or occasionally an industrial organization. He won't get rich, but if he is interested in medicine from the sociological as well as the biological point of view, he may find a highly satisfying and stimulating occupation in the public health field. Industrial, or as it is now called, "environmental," medicine is also offering a continually widening field.

Lastly I should like to apply the term "medical statesman" to certain of the careers that may more gradually open themselves to doctors of medicine. As governments and communities become more and more concerned with medical affairs, skilled leadership by medically trained persons will become increasingly important. The term medical statesman (in contrast perhaps to medical politician) conveys, I believe, the meaning I have in mind without further elaboration. Such people are needed for the high medical positions of government, as deans to medical schools, as directors of great medical centers, as editors of medical journals, in industry, and as leaders of health plans.

The decision to follow such a path will probably not be made early, but if the doctor is broadly educated in the first place and has the capacity for leadership, he may, in mid-career or earlier, find himself emerging into some such activity. It is to the best interest of the people that some of our ablest doctors of medicine be recruited into the field of medical statesmanship.

Such then very briefly is the general nature of the spectrum of professional opportunity offering itself to the young doctor of medicine. In making his choice of career he must look beyond the present and identify as clearly as possible the trend of development in medical affairs. I have tried to indicate some of these — the changing nature and growing importance of psychiatry, the need for better organization for the provision of medical care, better co-ordination of the services of generalists and specialists, better integration of teaching, research, and practice, and the development of leaders who will help all these things to come to pass.

5

General Medicine

by Donald M. Clark

THERE ARE THOUSANDS of general physicians and millions of their patients who are more than happy with their mutual relations and ask for no others. Nevertheless, this field is one of the most controversial in the world of medicine, and a volume would be required to present all phases of the many issues involved.

Even the name of the field and the title of its practitioners have been subjected to much discussion. "General practitioner," "family physician," "general physician," "local medical doctor," "personal physician," and "generalist" is a sample list attacked and defended by all branches of the profession. I have arbitrarily chosen the term "general medicine" to describe the field and "generalist" to identify the physician practicing in that area. The more complicated and important aspects, such as the definition of a generalist, the advantage of adequate and specific hospital training, definite qualifications for practice, the role of this practitioner in the field of surgery, and so on, are not so easily dealt with.

It is greatly to the advantage of some generalists, specialists, educators, and laymen to leave the nature of general medicine undefined in order to satisfy the fears, poses, prejudices, preconceptions, and hopes of some members of these groups. It requires much less effort and fewer people are offended if these vital problems are not met head on. As long as the nature of general practice remains uncertain, it will be impossible to reach an agreement about the extent of the general physician's participation in certain specialized fields. It will be equally impossible to establish the exact level of diagnostic and therapeutic responsibility.

Is the field of general medicine an anachronism when conducted at the highest level? There is statistical evidence to show that 75 per cent of pediatric care (in some areas 100 per cent) and 76 per cent of obstetric care (in some areas 90 per cent) are the responsibility of the generalists. There are no statistics dealing with general surgery, internal medicine, and a host of minor fields, but anyone who is familiar with rural, semirural, and small-city medicine knows that the major portion of the work in all of these areas at the community level is the responsibility of the generalist. The 1950 census revealed that 36.2 per cent of the population in this country live in rural areas (towns of 2500 or less). When the population of small cities cared for by generalists is added, it would seem that at least 50 per cent of the people call upon the generalist for their care. There are studies that have revealed that *well-trained generalists with adequate hospital, laboratory, and consultation services can and do care for approximately 85 per cent of all conditions met in their communities.* Granted that the above does not present the whole picture, there appears to be enough statistical evidence to prove that there is a vital place in medical practice for general medicine.

Theoretically, general medicine is in an enviable position, but the disquieting truth remains that, heretofore, *not more than 10 to 20 per cent of generalists were said to be competent,* judged by standards of excellent observers from their own field. This sad condition of affairs has improved but still is not satisfactory.

What follows is an attempt to summarize the various patterns of general medicine and the quality of the care it affords, and to formulate a definition of a qualified generalist. Finally, an attempt will be made to suggest certain programs of education and training and to indicate and analyze various locations that might be of interest to those who are considering entering this field.

PATTERNS OF GENERAL MEDICINE

Generalists may be placed in many categories, but three basic types seem to develop immediately, or a few years after, hospital training. The first (Class I) consists of those who have been inadequately trained for significant technical responsibilities by one year or less of "rotating" internships. The second (Class II) includes those who have been more nearly adequately trained by two or more years of internship-residency programs. The third (Class III) category consists of generalist-specialists, a very few of whom have had residency training but most of whom gradually develop from the first two classifications. A few may eventually become qualified specialists.

There are in addition, due to geographic considerations, five general patterns of practice: urban, suburban, small-city, semi-rural, and rural. Each of these patterns in turn may be classed as satisfactory or unsatisfactory in terms of quality of medical care.

URBAN PRACTICE

In the densely populated areas of our very large cities, the generalist who has been inadequately trained works in the midst of teaching hospitals and the best specialists available. He is not qualified for appointment to the staff of a recognized hospital, and his patients usually cannot afford to have private consultations. He works alone in his office virtually isolated from those in his field and the excellent specialists who surround him, except as he refers his patients to the teaching hospitals and clinics, where they are immediately lost to his view.

He depends upon volume and low fees and develops a rapid "spot diagnosis" technic that allows him to see, but not examine, a patient every five to fifteen minutes. He has no office assistants or laboratory facilities worthy of the name. The results of such a practice can be seen in the outpatient departments and wards of our teaching hospitals, where the terms "general practitioner" and "L.M.D." forever identify the generalist in the eyes of students, house staff, and educators as a physician of infirm status.

In this underprivileged medical environment is found an occasional physician whose training, conscience, and decency will not permit him to follow this path, and he may become quite closely, although not formally, connected with one of the teaching hospitals. An able diagnostician and therapist who hovers on the borderline of financial defeat may be the result of practicing excellent medicine in this environment.

Physicians from Class II (well-trained) are seldom found here unless they are forced into the pattern. Class III generalists (generalist-specialists) have no real place in this group. An excellent economic cross section of patients, together with good hospital affiliations, is necessary for the survival of the generalist-specialist.

SUBURBAN PRACTICE

As the thickly populated urban areas are left behind, the suburbs furnish quite a different picture. Here the inadequately trained man may receive an appointment to the staff of a good small local hospital on a trial basis. The more enlightened trustees of such hospitals will not allow him to perform major surgical procedures, but if he has a reasonably pleasing personality and is ambitious, conscientious, and hard-working, his worth may eventually be recognized. He has the opportunity of meeting personally the excellent consultants associated with such a local hospital, some of whom may have homes in that suburban area. If the generalist in question is reasonably well endowed with some of the attributes listed above, postgraduate educational programs will be devised for him, if he is interested. As he improves he will be recommended by the consultants and others to patients in all economic brackets in the area.

Lest this be thought a simple program, I should like to state categorically that it requires from *three* to *five years* of postgraduate study during practice to make up for the *loss of one year* of a residency program. The generalist with one year of internship training will require from six to ten years of conscientious postgraduate study, of approximately one or two months each year, to bring him to the level he would have attained following a properly conducted two-year residency program in internal medicine.

While this physician is attempting to compensate for the deficiency of his training, qualified specialists and better-trained generalists may be gradually added to the suburban community, and his economic and professional survival may become a race against time.

The suburban area close to teaching centers with a plethora of specialists, some of whom may have local offices, offers the keenest competition and calls for superior training for Class II generalists. This is one area in which two years' preparation in internal medicine, with added training in pediatrics and obstetrics, allows for gradual evolution. With such a background and proximity to a teaching center, the generalist can continue his medical education and qualify for the Board of Internal Medicine within ten years. This ability to effect a transition may become increasingly important in such an environment.

Generalist-specialists have a diminishing role in the suburbs, where young, fully trained surgeons, anesthesiologists, orthopedists, obstetricians, and pediatricians are immediately available, and where a large number of medically intelligent middle- and upper-class families often demand specialized attention in these and other fields because such services are so easily obtained.

SMALL-CITY PRACTICE

Although most of the conditions set out above under suburban practice also prevail in a small city, there are certain dissimilarities caused by increasing distance from medical centers and variation of medical development of the individual city. Some small urban areas may have a highly developed group of specialists working separately or as a clinic. Other cities, a few miles distant, may support only a qualified radiologist, a "visiting" pathologist, and one or more otolaryngologists. Without a good internist, surgeon, anesthesiologist, pediatrician, obstetrician, and so on in his area, the generalist may be forced to become increasingly familiar with some of these fields if he is separated by one or more hours from qualified specialists. Here, as in every other good environment, the superior training enjoyed by Class II is an advantage. In small-city practice Class III has responsibilities that depend entirely on how far the city has turned in the direction of specialism.

SEMIRURAL PRACTICE

For the purposes of this chapter, semirural practice indicates the type of work encountered in towns of approximately 3000 population, plus the surrounding towns, all served by one community hospital that furnishes care for a total population of from 10,000 to 20,000. Here there is a similarity to small-city and suburban medical practice, with one great difference — *there are few, if any, local specialists.* The population of this area may or may not be devoted to agriculture. In many Eastern areas large numbers of the original population have been displaced by a cosmopolitan population; they are financially solvent, medically intelligent, and quite ready to accept the only type of physician immediately available, if he is a generalist with a good reputation.

The physician who attempts to care for this group must be a competent diagnostician in internal medicine, general surgery, obstetrics, and pediatrics. His therapeutic range enables him to treat approximately 85 per cent of these patients at the level of a specialist, and he has a list of about a dozen specialists located in the nearest medical center with whom he works closely. These specialists are considered as much a part of his practice as the generalist himself.

Comparatively few of these men (one in twenty or less) perform major surgery. The office of such a physician is well organized, with a secretary, nurse, and technician, or some combination thereof, and his community hospital has excellent basic facilities. There is often a visiting radiologist and pathologist who has charge of radiology and the clinical laboratory.

How does this physician obtain his training? If he is to take these not inconsiderable responsibilities directly after hospital training, it will be to his advantage — if he does not perform major surgery — to have the equivalent of two years of internal medicine, during which he must have training in general surgical diagnoses through the emergency ward and outpatient department. He should have several months' additional experience in obstetrics and pediatrics — probably three to six months of each. An exceptionally good rotating internship of two years may be adequate. If he has the responsibility for general surgery, he should have three years of straight surgical training, followed by six months to one year of experience in general medicine, pediatrics, and obstetrics.

While a generalist with such broad responsibilities may be trained by postgraduate study following one year of rotating internship, *the time required is approximately six to fifteen years, depending upon his surgical responsibilities, his innate ability, and the amount of time he can give to postgraduate study.* He is accepted by the people and the specialists in the semirural situation because he is necessary to the first and noncompetitive to the second. He therefore develops all of his potentialities without artificial restraints.

It is in this situation that many generalists become qualified or semiqualified in various specialties (Class III). Such specialization may take place in suburban and small city areas if and when there are few specialists present; but hospital restrictions and other factors militate against such a course except in the field of internal medicine. In the semirural environment there is real necessity for a surgeon who can take responsibility for the many obstetric complications and be equipped to perform a creditable forceps delivery or a Caesarean section. There must be someone to perform emergency tracheotomies and operate on really acute abdominal conditions, in addition to caring for serious injuries at a certain level. Someone must be able to give endotracheal anesthesia, and routine and emergency electrocardiograms are a necessity. The generalists can and do carry out these assignments if they are well equipped by early hospital or continuous postgraduate study. No claim is being made that these procedures should be carried out by them if better-qualified men are available, but rapid transportation to regional hospitals will not solve all acute problems.

It must not be forgotten that the more interested the generalist becomes in a specialty, the less competent he may be as a generalist.

Emphasis has been placed on the generalist-specialist in the semirural area because this is one environment in which he is almost indispensable. However, all classes of generalists can fit in these areas, where everyone is welcome to an understaffed territory. Many such regions suffer chronically from lack of doctors, and conscientious practitioners of whatever training working together can practice remarkably good medicine. It is true that a few semirural regions have become highly specialized, but this is unusual and different from most patterns.

RURAL PRACTICE

Rural practice may be arbitrarily described as a type so isolated that it is impossible for the physician to reach the nearest hospital once or twice a day without jeopardizing other elements of his work. This type of practice in rural regions is usually spread for a distance of many miles in all directions, and it may require hours of motoring each day to care for patients. It is usually very difficult to organize a successful office practice where reasonably accurate diagnoses can be made. Sometimes this is because the physicians in this environment have made no attempt to educate their patients to come to them.

Of course, such a practice can be conducted at a high level, but the tendency seems to be for the generalist in these situations to deteriorate technically because he does not have the time for postgraduate study, there being no one with whom he can leave his practice. He does not have the daily contact with other physicians that is a constant source of postgraduate education. Furthermore, he does not take complete care of really ill patients, and in many instances this type of work resembles the highly unsatisfactory practice conducted by generalists in thickly settled urban areas. Physicians with Class II and III training might find their experience wasted in this particular environment, for obvious reasons.

DEFINITION OF A GENERALIST

In the first part of this chapter, reference was made to the lack of definition of general medicine. Because of this lack and the resulting ambiguities of status, limitations, and responsibilities, many young physicians are unwilling to take up what appears to be an outstandingly thankless form of medical practice. Such a situation gives rise to a vicious circle, harmful alike to the best interests of the medical profession and the public.

Is it possible to define what the qualified generalist must *know* and must *do?* This is quite possible and can be demonstrated initially by Figures 1 and 2, which are designed to show the real and practical diagnostic and therapeutic demands of general practice.

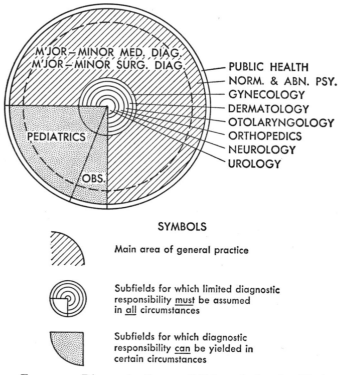

SYMBOLS

Main area of general practice

Subfields for which limited diagnostic responsibility <u>must</u> be assumed in <u>all</u> circumstances

Subfields for which diagnostic responsibility <u>can</u> be yielded in certain circumstances

FIGURE 1. Diagnostic Responsibilities of the Qualified Generalist (from the *New England Journal of Medicine* 248:143).

In these diagrams outstanding points to be noted are as follows: At least 75 per cent of the work in general practice falls into the fields of *major and minor medical and surgical diagnosis* and *major and minor medical treatment,* with undetermined overlapping into the field of psychiatry. Certain special fields can be, and frequently are, omitted from general practice. (This is important in terms of function and education of the general practitioner.) Certain special fields — principally psychiatry, dermatology, neurology, gynecology, orthopedics, otolaryngology,

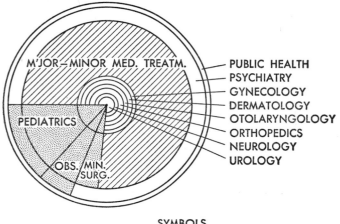

SYMBOLS

  Main area of general practice

  Subfields for which limited diagnostic responsibility <u>must</u> be assumed in <u>all</u> circumstances

  Subfields for which diagnostic responsibility <u>can</u> be yielded in certain circumstances

FIGURE 2. Therapeutic Responsibilities of the Qualified Generalist (from the *New England Journal of Medicine* 248:143).

and urology — cannot be omitted, being an essential part of all general practice. They are entered on the diagrams in such a way as to suggest their extent in general practice.

Before details of the full implications of all this are considered,

a concise and explicit definition of a general practitioner is necessary. The following definition is presented in terms of function,
not in the abstract terms so often used in previous attempts at
definition:

A generalist is a graduate in medicine from an approved
medical school who, after specific hospital training, is capable of
assuming responsibility for the following areas of medical care:

1. The diagnosis of all major and minor medical and surgical
conditions (except extremely complicated and rare ones).

2. The treatment of the great majority of the medical conditions diagnosed (but only the really *minor surgical* conditions).

3. *Obstetrics* to the level of uncomplicated deliveries, the early
recognition of abnormalities, and the necessarily immediate treatment of the few unpredictable but potentially catastrophic emergencies that may arise.

4. *Pediatrics* to the level required for medical and surgical diagnosis and treatment.

5. *Psychiatry* to a level permitting the differentiation of serious,
potentially serious, and mild psychoses and psychoneuroses, and
permitting the treatment of the last-mentioned by intelligent
support, clarification, and reassurance.

This definition, within broad limits, is specific in terms of
function and responsibility. However, like all definitions that
attempt to encompass a wide and diffuse range of activities,
events, or phenomena, it requires considerable explanation and
qualification. This cannot be attempted within the confines of
this chapter, and a full discussion of the generalist's responsibility
in general medicine will be found elsewhere (1).

It may be said, however, that the separation of medical and
surgical conditions, from a diagnostic standpoint, is arbitrary in
the field of general medicine. The various subfields have varying
relations to the whole: *Functional conditions* make up 36 per cent
or more of the problems. *Neurology* is very important because
errors in this field, such as the inability to recognize early menin-

gitis, subdural hematoma, and the like, may condemn the patient to an untimely death. *Obstetrics* has certain clear and immediate responsibilities implicit in the definition. *Gynecologic* diagnosis is so important that the generalist must accept broad and definite responsibilities in this area. *Dermatology, urology,* and *otolaryngology* have limited responsibilities. *Public health* duties are tenuous and variable except when associated with school medicine, maternity, and child welfare services.

The technics of *major surgery* are not here considered as a responsibility of the generalist. Incision and drainage of abscesses and the placing of a few skin sutures are thought to be his technical commitment except for diagnostic procedures (sigmoidoscopy, pelvic examinations, and so forth).

EDUCATION, HOSPITAL TRAINING, AND CHOICE OF LOCATION

"Teaching general practice" in medical schools and teaching hospitals would seem to be a process of bringing medical students into somewhat prolonged contact with excellent generalists who can demonstrate by precept their ability and the extent of the field of general medicine. Able generalists of this caliber are exceedingly hard to find. Such teaching can best be accomplished in the offices and community hospitals of the generalists, although outpatient departments and domiciliary care programs conducted by generalists are not to be ignored. The fourth-year student who is contemplating the field of general medicine is indeed fortunate if he has the opportunity of working with qualified generalists for a few weeks or months. Such a background and a definite idea of the specific community, or at least the type of community, desired allows the student to select hospital training suited for his future work.

A two-year rotating internship, which is recommended by qualified generalists, is probably the safest choice. If it seems inadequate, supplementary courses of from three to six months can be considered. Two years of internal medicine, including some pediatrics and experience in the emergency ward followed by three months of obstetrics, prepare generalists for specialist competition and eventual board qualification in internal medicine.

The day of learning basic major surgical technics in community hospitals is rapidly passing. If a medical student is firmly convinced that the community in which he is to practice requires a generalist-surgeon, he should prepare himself by three years of approved surgical residencies, adding six months to one year of medicine, obstetrics, and pediatrics as indicated. Such protracted training will, of course, require more time than preparation for some of the specialties, and the practical consideration of economic and professional compensation immediately arises. Careful evaluation of the one-to-three-year "general practice residencies" is necessary. Some of these programs are less than ideal, having been devised by excellent specialists who unfortunately have had no real experience in the field of general medicine.

One-year internships, on the other hand, can have real value if the intern drives himself day and night to obtain all possible experience. Unfortunately, many such programs are badly conceived, with "scut work" and "hospital services" predominating. Laborious, protracted, and expensive postgraduate studies can also compensate for lack of an adequate residency program.

Something should be said about preparation for group practice, regarding which there are two diametrically opposed viewpoints. One holds that a generalist has no place in a group of specialists, whereas opponents of this theory state that all patients should be first "screened" by generalists, whether in private clinics or outpatient departments. Practically, it may not be simple to balance specialists and generalists in the same group, but it can be accomplished. One great advantage that a group can offer the young generalist of too modest hospital training is increasing and controlled experience in close association with specialists and seasoned generalists.

An attempt to present the field of general medicine objectively must invariably result in a pessimistic note, because general medicine has been given less constructive thought and consideration by generalists, specialists, medical educators, and the public, than have other fields. This lack of consideration and understanding has placed general medicine in an unenviable position, but there are many indications of an increasing interest during the last decade. Some of the adverse criticism of the present is a holdover from the past and is not entirely valid.

It is evident that I am in no sense proselyting, and it is only fair to indicate some of the advantages of general medicine.

The well-trained generalist can offer intimate personal service to which the patient can turn for assistance in time of all physical and mental distress, and a sound, basic diagnostic and therapeutic service that will assure him a good first line of protection against the common hazards of illness and injury. This service can be offered by no other type of doctor, and such an opportunity is an unusually satisfying experience for many physicians. Some of the advantages of this field are that it can be practiced in many areas where the specialist cannot survive; that generalists who are financially handicapped are usually able to depend upon an immediate income, whereas some specialists may be forced to wait several years before they can become self-supporting; and that, in the rural and semirural areas especially, the excellent experienced generalist commands a place in his community enjoyed by few other people in the world.

If these concepts are approximately correct, it appears that the student who seriously considers entering this field should try to obtain several weeks or months of close association with a qualified generalist during his final year in medical school. He should be fairly convinced that first call for him is not a specialty, teaching, or research. He should very carefully select the community, or type of community, in which he desires to practice, and he should allow himself at least two and probably three years of hospital training. If circumstances make it necessary for him to spend only one year in hospital training and he is not in a rural area, he should be prepared, while practicing, to devote some time during the first six to ten years in intensive postgraduate study.

For those who voluntarily enter the field of general medicine, who really like their fellow beings and wish to serve them, and are willing to make more sacrifices than most persons are called on to make, general medicine can, if properly conducted, be as rewarding as any special field.

REFERENCE

1. COLLINGS, J. S. and CLARK, D. M. Medical Progress: General Practice, Today and Tomorrow. *New England Journal of Medicine* 248:141–148; 183–194 (January 22 and 29, 1953).

6

Specialty Practice

by Leland S. McKittrick

WHY SPECIALISTS?

Specialists are by-products of the science of medicine. As the latter has advanced, the opportunities offered for investigation of disease and methods of treatment have increased, and the knowledge gained in the various special fields has been so unlimited that specialization in areas of advancing knowledge or special technics has become necessary. That this logical and necessary trend would progress to the present state of almost complete fragmentation of the human body into systems or anatomical areas could hardly have been anticipated. How far specialization has developed at the present time, and how absurd it may appear is well illustrated by an incident that occurred recently in one of our better-known teaching institutions. This came to the writer's attention, not through the usual medical channels, but through a discussion group of Blue Shield executive directors. The method of division of the total fee when more than one surgeon was involved in a given operation was under discussion. The following incident was given as an example of the problem: A general surgeon in a well-known New England hospital had made a diagnosis of acute appendicitis in a young woman, but when the abdomen was opened it was found that she had an ovarian cyst with a twisted pedicle, rather than appendicitis. This condition, of course, fell within the field of gynecology. According to the rules of the hospital the general surgeon was not allowed to perform gynecological operations. It was necessary to call in a gynecologist to remove this ovarian cyst! The surgeon was then permitted to remove the appendix and close the abdomen. This concept of specialization is difficult to justify, but it is evidence of the degree of departmentalization that may occur under the conditions of specialization as we now know it.

If we accept this as an absurdity, how could it have come about? How important, after all, is specialization? If it is important and desirable, has the trend toward specialization now swung too far? At least a partial answer to these questions may be suggested by a review of the development of the specialty boards.

THE SPECIALTY BOARDS

According to the laws of most if not all of our states, there is no distinction among practicing physicians. Dr. Jones, who went into practice immediately following graduation from medical school, is legally privileged to perform any operation he may choose if he can get the patient's consent and secure hospital facilities. Formerly the public had no access to any information relative to the training, experience, and ability of a given physician in his or her specialty. It therefore seemed logical and desirable that some mechanism be set up for establishing minimum criteria for becoming recognized in various specialized fields. Thus, in 1916, the first specialty board was organized. Today every young medical school graduate who elects to go into a specialty looks forward to the time when he may receive certification in the specialty of his choice, and he plans his training program accordingly.

However, with the development of more and more specialty boards, training programs have been more demanding. The duration of many of these is now such that trainees are shunted from a thorough training in the fundamentals of good medicine or surgery into special fields, to a degree that at this time and probably in a large measure because of these boards, medicine has become so highly specialized that in many instances young men and women are becoming specialists without adequate knowledge of the basic problems in general medicine and general surgery.

Specialization, then, is a development of modern medicine. It is essential for the care of patients according to our present knowledge of disease and our present technical skills. It can be and has been carried to extremes. Will the trend toward more and more specialization continue, or has the pendulum made its full swing so that we will return to a closer co-ordination of the specialties with general medicine and surgery?

Most of the problems that arise in a patient following a hysterectomy are basically the same as those that follow a subtotal resection of the stomach. The knowledge necessary to evaluate and care for each patient is similar. To be sure, there are certain problems that are peculiar to each group of patients, but the basic principles involved in their surgical care are the same. The so-called general surgeon, the urologist, the gynecologist, and the thoracic surgeon should have knowledge of and experience in those basic problems that are common to all patients undergoing major surgical experiences. They should differ only in a superior knowledge of their own field.

The rapid increase in the number of specialties and their recognition by the approval of new specialty boards have been the source of deep concern to medical educators, leading clinicians, and to the Council on Medical Education and Hospitals of the American Medical Association. Instead of new boards, the present tendency is to require certification in the parent board (that of internal medicine or general surgery) and to recognize the specialty as a subsidiary to the Board of Internal Medicine or the Board of Surgery. Some of the surgical specialty boards are also gradually increasing the amount of training required in general surgery before specialization is begun. However, the harmful effects of overspecialization have already occurred. Their repair will be slow and difficult.

The specialty boards have two objectives: to establish minimum standards of graduate education and training requirements for physicians who represent themselves to the public as specialists, certifying those candidates who have qualified for and successfully passed the board's examination; and to improve the general standards of graduate medical education and the facilities for special training. In both of these objectives the boards have been eminently successful.

The American Board of Ophthalmology, created in 1916, was the first specialty certifying board. This was followed by the American Board of Otology in 1924, the American Board of Obstetrics and Gynecology in 1930, and the American Board of Dermatology and Syphilology in 1932. Other specialty groups became increasingly interested in the establishment of their own certifying boards. Each was anxious to take advantage of the experiences of those already formed, but each was also aware of the hazards and dangers that might go along with the spontaneous development of certifying boards, particularly without any real professional sponsorship. Consequently, during the years 1933 and 1934 the Advisory Board for Medical Specialties was organized and began to function. At the same time the House of Delegates of the American Medical Association passed a resolution authorizing the Council on Medical Education and Hospitals to formulate standards of administration for the specialty boards and to give new boards official recognition after they had been passed upon and recommended by the Advisory Board.

There are now eighteen separate boards listed in the *Directory of Medical Specialties* (the Board of Thoracic Surgery is a subsidiary board of the American Board of Surgery), with little reason to believe that this number will be increased in the immediate future.

The *Directory of Medical Specialists* has had six (1953) editions and lists 43,233 specialists who were certified prior to July, 1952. This is a living directory, but it does include those who may have retired from active practice. It is readily available in libraries, hospitals, and physicians' offices. It supplies rapid reference by both locality and name, and answers quickly "Who in this or that place holds the board certification?" or "Is Dr. So-and-So certified by a specialty board?" It is to be understood that a directory such as this can only certify that given physicians have fulfilled minimum training requirements and have passed the examinations of their boards. It may well be, and frequently is, true that in any city or town there are noncertified specialists whose experience and ability may exceed those of others who hold board certification. The latter in most instances will be older men who for one reason or another have felt that certification by their respective boards is not essential to them particularly since the technical aspects of examination are rather trying. Moreover, their formal training will in many instances be unacceptable to the boards. With the passage of time, however, there is reason to suppose that this group will gradually disappear and most of the qualified specialists will hold certification by their individual boards.

SPECIALTIES VERSUS GENERAL PRACTICE

Whether or not a physician specializes has a great deal to do with his income, the number of hours he works and where he lives. In general the specialist will settle in a larger city, will work fewer hours each week and earn more money in a year than the average general practitioner. The work week of the specialists in pediatrics and obstetrics, however, is longer than the 61-hour week of the general practitioner, and the work weeks in general surgery,

orthopedic surgery, and internal medicine are almost as long.
Moreover, the income of the general practitioner has increased
more rapidly during the past ten years than has that of the specialist, and the discrepancy between the two incomes continues to
decrease.

To select a specialty rather than general practice on a basis of a
shorter work week or higher income would be unrealistic and
improper. The demands of those who are sick or have recently
undergone operations will continue over week ends and holidays
and these demands must be met, not only by the general practitioner but frequently by the specialist.

The practice of medicine is not a life of undue sacrifice, nor is
it one of high income from a short working week. It is one of
devotion to sick people and their families and of responsibility to
individuals, to communities, to hospitals and to the profession.
Any graduate of a medical school who will successfully complete
a good graduate training program that prepares him for his particular job, who will devote himself to his work and accept his
full responsibilities either as a specialist or general practitioner,
will be rewarded financially as well as in the less tangible things
in life.

SPECIALTY TRAINING

I have already pointed out the absurd degree to which specialization may be carried, and suggested that many specialty training
programs have neglected training in the fundamental principles
of medicine and surgery. This has led to board certification of
many whose knowledge beyond that gained in medical school is
restricted to a special field of concentration. Such early total specialization is contrary to the thinking of most of those interested
in postgraduate medical education, and is difficult to defend in
the light of our present knowledge of the relation between disease
or trauma and the body as a whole.

Increasing recognition of the importance of a good training in general medicine and general surgery before specializing in one of the subdivisions of either undoubtedly will greatly influence the specialty boards in determining their future requirements. Therefore, the young medical school graduate anticipating a specialty in the clinical branches of medicine should look forward to a thorough training in the problems of general medicine or surgery before getting the special training in one of the subdivisions. This means a minimum of hospital training of from four to six years after the year of internship. Hospital training is particularly emphasized here, although it is recognized that the number of training programs that accept the young graduate and see him through a complete and carefully integrated program preparing him for board certification are all too few. It is the recognition of this fact that has prompted certain certifying boards to accept a portion of training requirements under a preceptor. Experience has shown, however, that few if any practicing surgeons or physicians at this time are able to give the young graduate the breadth of experience that is available to him in a large general hospital. No general surgeon today can give the young man or woman the experience in emergency work, fractures, urology, thoracic surgery, surgery of the endocrine glands, and so on, that is a part of his training in a good hospital training program.

An excellent example of the present concept of board certification in the subspecialties is evidenced by the recent action of the American Board of Surgery following a request for a board of trauma. With our present knowledge of the effect of trauma upon the entire organism and with the multiplicity of injuries that occur as a result of modern transportation, to be a qualified specialist in trauma a surgeon must be trained to treat the patient who has had the accident, not just the fractured femur or the ruptured bladder. Therefore before such an applicant can be certified as a specialist in trauma, he must have demonstrated his training and experience in general surgery by being certified by the American Board of Surgery. Then if his training and experience permit, he could have a subsequent examination in the surgery of trauma and receive a special certificate from the Board of Surgery, not from a separate board of trauma. This undoubtedly will be the pattern of subsequent specialties in either medicine or surgery as they may develop.

INTRODUCTION TO PRACTICE

The transition from resident specialist to practicing specialist may be easy or difficult. Those young men and women completing good board qualifying training programs in several of the so-called subclinical specialties, such as radiology, pathology, and anesthesiology, have little difficulty in finding attractive openings with excellent remuneration. The demand is still in excess of the supply of good, well-trained men. Most of the work is done in hospitals, and one has but to accept a position in an area of need and a busy practice is readily available.

This is not true in many of the other specialties, especially those in which there is a direct responsibility of physician to patient.

Probably the most difficult specialty in which to develop a successful practice is that of major surgery. The patient may be willing to have an X-ray examination, or to be given anesthesia, or even to be treated medically by a young practitioner. But even in the young man's world of today the average person likes to know a little something of the surgeon who is to perform a serious operation.

The young surgeon so fortunate as to develop an association with an older established board-certified surgeon who will be interested in his development, or one who may be asked to join a successful medical group, is spared much of the hardship of those who have no such opportunity. To go from a busy surgical residency to the inactive role of a young surgeon just starting his own practice may prove very discouraging.

In a good training program every effort is made to give to the resident the best possible training. The emphasis is upon education, not service. Young men in surgery are given opportunity to make decisions and to perform the actual operations, at first under experienced supervision, carrying out the simpler, less serious procedures. As the experience and technical ability of the young surgeon increase, he is permitted to do more and more complicated operations until by the time his training is completed he carries, with only a minimum of direct supervision, the responsibility for most of the patients who are admitted to his service. At the end of a good four-year graded resident program he has become an accomplished surgeon, capable of successfully completing any of the surgical procedures that are being done. Moreover, scarcely a day passes that he does not perform one or more extensive operations. The patients upon whom he is operating have come under his care through no effort on his part. They have come to the hospital in which he is working; the members of the visiting staff of the hospital have trained him to carry out the operations and then have made available to him the patients who need them. As a result of this extended training program an excellent product has been developed. Having acquired the training, however, each surgeon must seek his own market. None has been prepared for him.

It is not easy for the young surgeon, who may have spent five or six years after graduation preparing to practice the specialty of his choice, to make the necessary adjustment from the protected life of a resident surgeon to the hazards and trials associated with a competitive practice. Formerly everything possible was done to help him; now every possible resistance may be put in his way — difficulty in obtaining hospital privileges, or the necessity of working under supervision of an established but less competent man. In some areas it may even be suggested that unless he refunds to the referring physician a portion of the surgical fee, his services will not be needed. His hospital training did not quite prepare him for these and other problems he must now face and overcome.

These young men know what they are capable of doing. They do not realize that neither the public nor the potential referring physician shares this knowledge, and that until they have become known locally and are able to win the confidence and respect of the local community, the opportunities for them to demonstrate their ability will be infrequent. Now, when they have the least to do, they must be at their busiest. Always available for emergency calls, interested and active in local hospital, medical society, and community activities, they must in a quiet and efficient manner become a vital part of the community in which they have chosen to live.

To the degree that they know their own training and skills in their specialty, they must have confidence in themselves and in their future. This, together with an untiring interest in their work, an understanding of people, and a true desire to co-operate with and wherever possible to be helpful to their new associates can but result in the success that is their due.

REFERENCES

1. Rusk, H. A., Diehl, H. S., Barclay, R. W., and Kaetzel, P. K. The Work Week of Physicians in Private Practice. *New England Journal of Medicine,* October, 1953.
2. Maurer, Herryman. The M.D.'s Are Off Their Pedestal. *Fortune,* February, 1954.
3. Income of Physicians. Survey by the United States Department of Commerce and the American Medical Association, 1949.
4. Survey by *Medical Economics,* Rutherford, N. J., 1952, reports published in December, 1952, and April, 1953, issues.

7

Group Practice

by Edwin P. Jordan

Wʜᴀᴛ ᴇxᴀᴄᴛʟʏ is meant by the term group practice? Actually, it cannot be strictly defined, and no matter what description is employed, wide variation in size, mode of practice, structure, location, and other features will be encountered.

One definition (1) has it that ". . . group practice consists of a number of physicians and dentists who combine their professional services, skills, and financial resources to practice the prevention and treatment of disease. These practitioners use common offices, facilities, and professional equipment. They employ in common subsidiary personnel for administrative and clinical purposes." Another (2) says: "Medical group practice is a formal association of three or more physicians providing services in more than one medical field or specialty, with income from medical practice pooled and redistributed to the members according to some prearranged plan."

For purposes of eligibility for full membership, the American Association of Medical Clinics states in its bylaws: "Any group of seven or more full-time physicians maintaining a private organization for the purposes of providing general medical care of high quality . . . shall be eligible for membership. Such group or clinic shall have on its full-time staff at least five physicians in different major specialties, two of which specialties shall be internal medicine and general surgery. Such group shall maintain a separate building or suite of offices for the conduct of its practice."

These descriptions indicate, at least in a general way, what is meant by group practice.

There are several methods by which group practice clinics may be classified — by size, by nature of services rendered, or by internal structure and organization. Some are mammoth, with physician staffs ranging into the hundreds. Others are small partnerships of three or four men; probably the majority occupy an intermediate position so far as size is concerned. Some provide the immediate community with medical service in much the same manner as do individual or solo practitioners, whereas others are principally groups of specialists engaged in referral work and consultations. The majority serve both these functions.

Most groups consist of practitioners who have banded together into private organizations. In some instances physicians connected with a hospital or medical school have joined in what is surely one kind of group practice. Some groups are sponsored by consumers and are usually known by the name of health cooperatives. In a few cases the establishment of prepaid medical care programs has led to the development of medical groups designed to care for the patients enrolled under such insurance plans. In some instances the physicians in a group are all in one specialty such as radiology, internal medicine, or dermatology. All the physicians in some group practice clinics are specialists in various fields; in others physicians in general practice play an important part; some of them are comprised exclusively of general practitioners.

DEVELOPMENT AND GROWTH

Many factors have led to the formation of group practices. Among them are included the great increase in specialty practice in the last thirty years and the influence of both world wars.

Of 330 listed groups in 1940, 25 per cent were organized within the five-year period of 1919 to 1923, compared with 21 per cent before 1919 (3). When polled during the last year of World War II, over one-half of the physicians in the United States military services indicated that they wished or intended to join groups on their return to civilian life.

Although accurate figures concerning the development of new group practices are not available, it is significant that at least 368 medical groups existed in 1946, and 91 additional groups came to the attention of the Public Health Service between that year and 1951 (2).

For the same reason that it is almost impossible to define and identify all group practices, it is difficult to know how many physicians are practicing in groups. One analysis indicates that approximately 2 per cent of all practitioners are full-time physicians on the staffs of groups as shown in 1940 and 1946 studies — 2093 and 3275 physicians respectively. Hunt and Goldstein (2) estimated that there were about 5000 physicians in full-time group practice in 1950 — about 3 per cent of all practicing physicians. Although the statement cannot be accurately documented, it is beyond doubt that both the numbers of group practice units have increased since 1946 and the proportion of physicians in such forms of practice also has grown.

A survey (4) in 1950 and 1951 of 52 group practice organizations in California indicated that about 60 per cent of these groups were in communities of less than 50,000 population. Many of the groups were small, the average number of physicians in a group being six or seven.

Over 70 per cent of the 74 larger groups that were members of the American Association of Medical Clinics in mid-1953 were located in communities with populations under 125,000.

According to Hunt (5): "The principal advantage claimed for group practice is that modern medicine is so complex that no one physician can comprehend all the niceties of diagnosis and treatment, that as a result of this situation most sick people — if they are to get the best medical care — must be seen by more than one physician and that organization of physicians into groups is the only way in which this can be done efficiently and economically. It is claimed that physicians working together in a group are stimulated to keep up with medical progress more than physicians in individual practice and that each physician, constantly subjected to the informal appraisal of his fellows, has more incentive to do his best work and is less likely to develop slipshod habits of medical practice. The ease and value of consultations is enhanced because the consultant has the patient's whole medical record before him and can more quickly and efficiently bring his own special knowledge to bear on the case. On the financial side a group of men, by pooling their resources, can maintain equipment for diagnosis and treatment that no one of them could maintain individually and can make efficient use of such expensive items as X-ray equipment. Physicians' incomes are more stable and some claim that they are larger than incomes in individual practice, at least in the early and late years of practice. The physician in a group is freed from direct financial dealings with patients and is therefore able to do his best work medically without worry about whether he will be paid. He is enabled to take vacations and trips for postgraduate study without jeopardizing his practice or his future prospects. The patient benefits by less expensive service (the usual claim is that he gets more service for the same cost than he would get from an individual practitioner), as well as by the ready availability of competent consultation when he needs it. A well run group is alleged to raise the medical standards of the whole community by exemplifying modern medical care. Groups have the facilities for, and tend to stress, preventive medicine. By providing nursing and secretarial help economically group organization enables the doctor to spend more of his time doing medical work and relieves him of work that can be done as well or better by less highly trained personnel. A final claim is that group practice facilitates the organization and efficient operation of prepayment plans."

Except in a very few states a corporation cannot practice medicine. For this reason the vast majority of group practice clinics are organized as partnerships. Again the variation in the details of such partnership agreements is remarkable. Some consist of two or three original partner-founders with the other physicians in the group serving as employees of the partnership. More commonly a definite pattern of entry into the partnership is available for physicians joining the group. A trial period averaging between two and three years before admission to the partnership is common, but not invariable. Sometimes a junior partnership has been established as a step preceding the attainment of full-partnership status.

Another aspect of most partnerships that should be mentioned is that the more experienced groups have generally found it not feasible to continue indefinitely an equal division of income among the partners, nor even to weight the influence of each partner in the affairs of the group exactly alike. Consequently, many devices have been adopted to make the partnership structure fit into a smoothly functioning operation. If a corporation could legally practice medicine it would have numerous advantages over the partnership, especially for the groups of larger size. Since it usually cannot, however, a "new" form of group practice has begun to develop. This is an organization that can be described briefly as an unincorporated association of physicians. This structure permits all the physicians in the group to be on a salary established by an elected board of trustees or governors, and therefore it can be operated in much the same manner as a corporation. In this variety of clinic organization, also, new physicians added to the group are generally taken on at the beginning as employees of the association before they are elected to full membership. The association provides considerable flexibility and ease of administration lacking in the partnership, and is claimed to facilitate continuity and the coming and going of physician members.

PROBLEMS OF ORGANIZATION

The physician contemplating joining a group practice clinic is well advised to have in advance some understanding of the advantages, disadvantages, and problems of such association in comparison with individual practice. If the various factors are understood, faced, and evaluated beforehand rather than after two or three years of practice with a clinic, much unhappiness and dissatisfaction may be avoided.

The most important problem in the successful operation of a group is the establishment of an equitable and reasonably satisfactory method for the division of the net professional earnings. It is the writer's opinion that there is no "perfect" method of dividing earnings in the sense that every single physician in a group will be satisfied at all times that he is receiving his just deserts. Nevertheless, there are certainly some methods that are much more satisfactory than others.

One method that is employed, at least occasionally, is to divide all net earnings exactly equally among the partners. This has, of course, the advantage of simplicity, but ultimately the earning power, because of specialty and the degree of application of the physicians in a group, will diverge to such an extent that some will justly feel that they are underpaid for their contribution to the group even though the others may not feel that they are overpaid! As a long-term proposition this equal division of net earnings is probably impractical.

Successful group practice clinics have developed a great number of different methods of determining what the income of each partner or physician member of the group should be. Some methods consist of complicated systems in which a certain number of points are assigned to each physician member on the basis of such factors as bookings, age, length of time with the clinic, attraction of new patients, number of referrals, professional standing, and many other qualities both tangible and intangible. It should be said that these methods have been designed in order to achieve the equity that is generally desired. Some of them seem to work with reasonable success.

More commonly, perhaps, a larger group practice clinic will have among its members an executive or finance committee which determines the income of each member of the group on the basis of an evaluation of the contribution of each physician. Roughly the same factors often used in the point system are employed under this method also. This method has some advantages in flexibility over the point system; it permits a physician who feels he has not been adequately remunerated to meet with the committee determining his income and present his point of view, and that committee may in turn explain the reasons that determined its decisions. It matters little, in practice, whether the division of income is managed in this manner under a partnership arrangement or when all physicians are on a salary, and salary and bonus are adjusted according to the same criteria. Certainly the physicians in a group should not expect perfection from any method they adopt to divide their income, but should attempt to make it work as well as possible.

There is one other matter that every physician entering group practice should consider in connection with his expected earnings. If he is a young man entering a properly managed group practice clinic, he can expect what amounts to a ready-made practice, with little or none of the initial waste of his professional time that often occurs when he starts in practice by himself. Nevertheless, the introduction of a new physician into a group lowers the income of the other members, at least during the first year or two of his association, and for this reason he should expect in the subsequent few years some lag between his earning capacity and his take-home income.

Furthermore, it is during the middle professional years of high earning potential that most physicians become unhappy — if they do — in a group practice clinic. This is because they see colleagues and classmates in individual practice in the same field who may be earning a great deal more. In all probability, however, given two equally competent and successful physicians, one in group practice and the other in solo practice, *the lifetime earnings* after overhead and taxes are deducted would differ very little. The income of the group practice physician is likely to be higher at the beginning of his professional career, lower in the middle years, and reduced less rapidly in the later years of his professional career. At any rate, these factors and probabilities should be frankly considered in advance and the choice taken with one's eyes open.

Enough has been said already to indicate that entry into group practice does not guarantee a bed of roses and that it presents many continuing problems as well as advantages. Perhaps because of the innumerable difficulties in establishing a group practice clinic, many of those now in existence have been and some are still operated as one-man autocracies. The autocratic head of a group must battle through many of the problems mentioned — and others — and often can do so more efficiently and effectively than can a more amorphous group structure. The fact that there is only one head of the group and that all unresolved matters are referred to and decided by him frequently leads to smooth functioning even though associated with much grumbling. There is little doubt that many group practice clinics would not be alive today if it had not been for the forceful and successful efforts of autocratic founders.

In the nature of things an autocratic structure, if it was the original form, cannot continue indefinitely. When the time comes for it to change, a crisis often faces the clinic. The pressures for increased democracy or representation by the professional staff are generally irresistible; but if leadership is lacking, a state of utter confusion may arise. Without going into the technical problems involved, it can be said only that this phase of evolution involves a compromise between the desirable features of democratic representation and the necessary development of leadership and administrative abilities. That this has been accomplished so successfully in so many places offers testimony to the feasibility of such an evolutionary process.

With increasing frequency group practice clinics are establishing fringe benefits of considerable value to the physician: time off and financing for medical meetings or graduate courses, specified time for sick leave and vacations, group life insurance, and most recently, efforts to develop satisfactory pension plans. The nature of these benefits of association with a group vary, of course, from one to another, but are factors to be taken into consideration by the members of the professional staff as well as the nonprofessional employees.

Some groups rent office space in a building more or less indefinitely and thus have a problem differing little from that of the individual physician, who must also pay rent. The majority of the private clinics, however, have considerable investment in buildings and equipment, usually built up by capital paid in by the physicians in the group. In some instances the investments are extremely large, which poses a problem when an original partner or member retires, dies, or leaves the group, or when a new physician joins it. In a similar way the setting up of reserve for expansion and the purchase of new equipment frequently presents a problem.

Many devices have been adopted to facilitate the orderly transfer of capital from older to younger physicians. Some are more successful than others. At the present time, in private medical clinics, there is an increasing tendency to manage this problem through the medium of a corporation or nonprofit foundation separate from the partnership. As time goes on the problem is apparently being solved with greater and greater success. The necessity for so doing is the greater because of the difficulty with which even successful younger physicians are faced in saving enough from their incomes to invest in capital expenses in the present days of high income taxes.

None of the problems enumerated, or others with which group practice clinics are commonly faced, seem to be insoluble. However, both the group as an entity and the professional individuals in it must have a desire to meet the problems as they arise and to make things work, or insurmountable difficulties may develop.

POSSIBILITIES FOR THE FUTURE

The development of group practice is a strictly North American contribution to the mechanics of rendering medical care, and a partial answer to the growth of specialism during the past half century. It gives every evidence of being here to stay, though its patterns of development are still in process of evolution and presumably several different forms will eventually emerge as being best adapted to differing circumstances.

It is significant that this development has resulted in the establishment of two national organizations in the field of group practice: the National Association of Clinic Managers, and the American Association of Medical Clinics. The business aspects connected with the operation of a successful group of physicians are obviously considerably more complicated than those of an individually practicing physician. The first organization in the field, therefore, was the National Association of Clinic Managers, which was established in 1926. It testified to the fact that all other aspects of group practice would fail unless there was enough money available to pay the medical and nonmedical personnel and for equipment and services. This association has held annual meetings and has collected a vast amount of information on the business aspects of group practice. It has rendered the medical profession great service in gathering information concerning appropriate business methods and in standardizing certain types of business procedures. There is no foreseeable end to the contribution that this organization can make to the field of business management as related to group practice.

The American Association of Medical Clinics, an organization of group practice clinics in the United States and Canada at the professional level, was established in 1949. Its purposes are: to elevate the standards of practice in medical clinics; to foster and improve graduate medical education in such clinics; to promote medical research in such clinics; to give mutual help by the interchange of ideas and experiences of member clinics; and to disseminate scientific and medical knowledge, particularly as such knowledge pertains to the practice in medical clinics. Some of its activities are consequently significant for physicians considering entry into group practice.

The American Association of Medical Clinics holds an annual meeting at which many problems peculiar to group practice are discussed, including internal structure and organization of groups, their relation to prepaid medical care plans, and similar matters of special interest. The proceedings of these meetings and other information are published in the association's bulletin (6) currently issued six times a year.

This association issues a directory of its members, giving the professional staff members and their fields of specialty. It is actively pursuing a study of the role of group practice clinics in the provision of graduate medical education, in conjunction with the Council on Medical Education and Hospitals of the American Medical Association and the Advisory Board of Medical Specialties. Likewise, it is engaged, with the Council on Medical Service of the American Medical Association, in a survey of group practice, aimed at developing information that would be of value to physicians desiring to start a group practice, or to group practice clinics that have problems with which they need assistance.

Finally, of interest to some is the placement service offered by the association to physicians desiring to enter a group practice, and to group practice clinics that desire additional professional personnel. These constitute only a few of the activities in which this association has become involved in its brief existence.

In summary, group practice offers attractions to the practicing physician in many respects; it probably aids in providing improved medical care to many communities, but poses many problems of operation. The number of group practice units and the number of physicians associated with this form of practice are both increasing, but at a modest rate.

REFERENCES

1. MOORE, J. E. Staff Offices as Tried Alternative to Group Care. *Hospitals* 17:47 (1943).
2. HUNT, G. H. and GOLDSTEIN, M. *Medical Group Practice in the United States*. Public Health Service Publication No. 77 (1951).
3. *Group Medical Practice*. Publication of the Bureau of Medical Economics, American Medical Association (1940).
4. WEINERMAN, E. and GOLDSTEIN, G. S. *Medical Group Practice in California*. From the Division of Medical Care Administration, School of Public Health, University of California, Berkeley (1952).
5. HUNT, G. H. Medical Group Practice in the United States. *New England Journal of Medicine* 237:71–77 (1947).
6. Bulletins, American Association of Medical Clinics, Charlottesville, Va.

8

Doctor and Hospital

by Alfred Kranes

GENERAL CONSIDERATIONS

To the physician about to start practice, the remarks that follow may seem superfluous, since such a large part of his medical career has been spent within hospital walls. However, he will soon discover an essential difference between being a member of the hospital community, and being a member of the community that the hospital serves. It is necessary to keep this distinction in mind, for the hospital does not exist primarily for the doctor's benefit, even though he may be one beneficiary of its policies and services.

It would be helpful, before considering the doctor's place in it, to remind ourselves of the reasons for the hospital's existence. Its primary purpose is the care of the sick. As subsidiaries to this main function it should further medical education and promote research and investigation. The degree to which these three aims are attained will depend to a large extent on the type of hospital. The smaller community hospitals are devoted almost exclusively to caring for the ill, whereas the large teaching hospitals have extensive teaching programs, including not only undergraduate and postgraduate medical instruction, but nursing schools and training courses for dietitians, social workers, and others. In the teaching hospitals also, medical research is highly organized under the supervision of specialists, usually in conjunction with a medical school. But teaching and research need by no means be confined solely to the teaching hospitals, although nowhere else can they be carried on to such an extensive degree. Medical investigation can be and is being carried on in community hospitals. Here, however, it is more likely to be sporadic, unorganized, and dependent on the curiosity or initiative of individual members of the staff. As with investigation, so too with teaching in the smaller community hospitals, where the education of nurses, interns, and colleagues may present opportunities, smaller in scope but nevertheless vital to the institution. Wherever one is, similar opportunities, though varying in degree, can be found if one searches for them.

It should be remembered that the hospital represents a community need for the care — usually temporary — of its sick and disabled members. The doctor is only one instrument, albeit an important one, for returning these persons to their customary activities in as short a period of time as possible.

Most hospitals are run by an administrator, either lay or medical, or by a registered nurse, under the supervision of some sort of governing board or trustees, who generally represent a cross section of the best citizens that the community provides. There may be a physician or two on the board, but the majority will and should be laymen. Doctors frequently complain about this, remarking that laymen do not properly understand the problems of the medical profession. However, it is highly improbable that a hospital run exclusively by physicians would be as responsive to the needs of a given community as a more representative group, embodying varying shades of opinion. It is true that hospital governing boards occasionally render decisions appearing arbitrary and unfortunate to the medical staff, but the doctors will make their relations with the hospital more harmonious by bearing in mind two important facts. In the first place, doctors represent a very small segment of the whole community. Secondly, although they are the agents into whose skilled hands the community's health is entrusted, it is the community, as represented by the hospital governing board, whose judgment must prevail. That is not to say that the doctors should be passive agents. On the contrary, they should be — and frequently are — quite vocal; but it would be less fortunate for most hospitals if the doctors' voices were the exclusive ones.

To return to the physician who has just completed his hospital training and is about to start his practice. Until now his time has been spent acquiring the skills that will shortly be put to use. He has been an important part of a comparatively small hospital group having a common professional interest. It was an uncommonly homogeneous group, despite the widely divergent backgrounds of its members, knit together by a unifying interest in medicine. When he leaves this group to become a member of the much larger and more heterogeneous one in the community of his choice, his relation with his new (or even with the same) hospital will be a different one.

One of the first steps to be taken by the physician starting in practice will be to seek affiliation with a hospital, since he will stifle medically without it. Indeed, one of the disconcerting aspects of the British National Health Service has been the divorce of the general practitioners from the hospital. That they are none too happy about this state of affairs, now going on for about five years, is apparent from a perusal of almost any issue of the *Lancet* or the *British Medical Journal*. The sudden deprivation of their hospital connections has forcefully imposed a new way of life on British practitioners and many of them do not like it. As the experiment proceeds, perhaps a way will be found to modify the present scheme in Britain and to give the general practitioners some access to hospitals. It would seem a safe assumption that if this is not done the caliber of general practice is likely to deteriorate in time.

What then are the reasons that make a hospital affiliation so vital to the doctor? It is obvious that it is the only place offering the diagnostic facilities for his more complex problems, and helping him care for those of his sicker patients who cannot be adequately cared for in their homes. This is especially true, of course, with patients requiring surgery. But it offers him much more than that. Aside from the facilities it provides for the care of his patients, the hospital is one of the most vital elements in the doctor's postgraduate education. "The education of the doctor is not a mere by-product of the care of the sick" (1). The opportunities presented will depend on various factors: whether it is a teaching hospital, the size and caliber of the staff, and how much planning has been devoted to the formulation of an educational policy. But even in the smallest hospitals, where no specific plan exists, the doctor's education proceeds, even if in a formless manner, by means of consultations, discussions with his colleagues on medical problems of mutual interest, and staff meetings. The educational value of such informal contacts with his medical brethren will depend to a considerable degree on these physicians' capabilities, sagacity and astuteness. Given the proper ingredients, the value of even these casual discussions must not be underestimated.

Finally, and not to be overlooked as vital elements in the doctor's education, are the intern and resident. The intern and resident are there to learn, to be trained, as well as to assist the staff members to the best of their capabilities. They bring to the hospital a fresh point of view, a mass of new information recently imparted by their teachers. They are anxious to learn and will ask many questions, some of them quite penetrating. In answering these questions one is forced to formulate and organize one's own ideas, to reject what once seemed acceptable when it does not withstand closer scrutiny. One learns that there is nothing more stimulating and provocative than contact with a young and inquisitive mind. I can imagine nothing more dreary than laboring alone, out of contact with what even the most meager hospital may have to offer the doctor, aside from the care of his patients.

HOSPITAL CARE OF PRIVATE PATIENTS

The hospital care of his private patients will occupy a variable amount of the doctor's time, depending on the type of work he is doing. For the surgeon it will be much more than for the ophthalmologist or dermatologist. Which patients to hospitalize is frequently a more difficult decision than it at first appears, since it may involve much more than the immediate illness. If an operation is required there is, of course, no problem about where it should be done, for the days of kitchen table surgery are fortunately a thing of the past. But for those in general practice or internal medicine, it may not be quite so simple.

Although the care of the patient is the primary duty of the doctor, it is well to remember that this occasionally conflicts with his convenience. Getting as many of his patients as possible under one roof greatly simplifies his own problems, even though it may complicate those of his patients and their families. Fortunately there is a formidable economic brake opposing such tendencies at present, with the costs of hospitalization so high. This deterrent to indiscriminate hospitalization serves a useful purpose, except in those cases where necessary hospital care may be unduly delayed because of the expense involved.

With the constantly increasing use of hospital insurance plans, however, and the elimination, either partial or complete, of the financial barrier, it becomes more than ever the doctor's duty to see that no unfair advantage is taken of these facilities. The ultimate success of private medical insurance schemes will depend on their cost. Anything that raises their cost, such as overgenerous hospitalization, is an invitation to the state to provide it "free" in the form of compulsory insurance. With so many in the community now carrying medical insurance of some sort, it is by no means an easy matter to resist the pressures for hospitalization, particularly when diagnostic problems are encountered. The decision may not be easy, but hospitalizing a patient solely because his X-ray examinations or other diagnostic tests will be paid for by an insurance company is to be condemned.

The skill and self-assurance of the physician, as well as the trust the family places in him, will often determine whether he sends the patient to a hospital or treats him at home. All patients should be treated at home whenever possible. The physician should appreciate the importance of the fears and anxieties evoked within a patient and his family when hospital admission is advised, to say nothing of the disruption of normal family life, and the expense. All this must be weighed against the possible advantages of the move. Hospitalization may sometimes be advised to protect the doctor from criticism, in cases where the illness may take a turn for the worse. For some reason the doctor seems less blameworthy if the patient dies in the hospital and not at home. However, little weight should be given to this consideration if hospital treatment offers no real prospect of palliating the disease or appreciably prolonging life.

The problem of whether or not to hospitalize will frequently arise, for example, in cases of myocardial infarction, where sudden death is an ever present possibility. There are a few genuine advantages in treating such patients in a hospital. These include the controversial benefits of anticoagulant therapy, the prompt and vigorous treatment of acute pulmonary edema, and the prompt treatment of serious cardiac arrhythmias occurring during convalescence. How efficacious and prompt such therapy may be will, of course, depend on the training and alertness of the intern and resident staff. In a teaching hospital with a well-organized resident staff, it may be superb — and lifesaving. In a community hospital without well-trained interns, such benefits may be nonexistent. Furthermore, the contemplated benefits must be weighed against the hazards, usually intangible and difficult to evaluate.

Returning to the patient with an acute myocardial infarct, seen one to two hours after the onset of his pain and sent promptly to the hospital after the customary injection of an opiate, can one be certain that he is not being harmed? What about the inevitable anxiety and apprehension engendered? Might the expense unduly concern him? Will he be unhappy in his new environment among the strange people who now surround him? We do not know the effect of all these far from nebulous factors on the mortality of myocardial infarction treated in the hospital. Perhaps we shall never know, since information of this sort is not easy to come by. But it cannot be beneficial. Similar considerations are involved in many other acute illnesses.

There are additional factors that must influence the decision of home versus hospital care, such as the type of home. Does the patient live alone, and can he receive the necessary nursing care? If he lives with his family, are they willing and able to look after his needs? Will the presence of noisy children or well-meaning but often interfering relatives and friends hamper his recovery? It is quite apparent that the decision is often not a simple one. Whenever possible the patient should be treated at home — if that is the wish of his family and himself — providing that his recovery is not impeded, and that hospital care can contribute nothing of real significance. The fact that a patient suffers from a fatal disease is not *ipso facto* a necessary reason for moving him out of his home.

To facilitate the care of his private hospital patients and make the transition from home to hospital easy for them, the doctor should exercise as much foresight as possible in arranging for their stay. He should avoid, for example, admitting patients on Sundays, holidays, or during the evenings, unless there is a real emergency. At such times most hospitals are less well staffed for receiving patients. Nor will the experienced physician send his patient to a hospital for diagnostic study during the latter half of the week. He knows that on Saturday afternoon and Sunday the X-ray and other laboratories are able to do only emergency work, and that a day and a half have been wasted for the patient.

The physician should also see to it that medical orders or instructions either accompany the patient or are made available promptly after the patient's arrival, so that the nursing staff will know precisely what to do. All too frequently, the nurses are kept in the dark for hours concerning such simple things as whether or not to keep a patient in bed or what to feed him, if anything. Often it will make little difference, but at other times it may be quite important. But whether important or not, the relations among the three parties — doctor, patient, and hospital — will be enormously helped if the nurses are instructed what to do when the patient arrives. One wonders too, what patients think of the doctor who sends them to the hospital without providing promptly for their care.

Although it is not the purpose of this section to suggest what to prescribe for patients, it is important to take note here of one of the hazards of hospital prescribing, since we are concerned with the care of the private hospital patient. It is more likely to involve patients who have been in the hospital for some time. Whenever any medication has been ordered, aside from opiates, the patient will go on receiving it unless the order is specifically discontinued. The amount of medicine being given to some patients who have been in the hospital several weeks may be appalling, as one agent after another is tried to improve their condition. Many fevers have been cured by omitting all medication rather than adding more. This is equally true of skin rashes, as well as a variety of gastrointestinal complaints. Such overmedication is less likely when the patient is treated at home, where every new prescription will doubtless evoke a question from either the patient or his family concerning the advisability of also continuing the old one. To avoid this hospital hazard, it would be wise to review, at least weekly, all the medication a patient is receiving, omitting whatever is not considered essential at the moment.

If I have concerned myself unduly with the avoidance of certain mistakes when patients are hospitalized, it is because I cannot give advice on what to do in any given case. I can suggest what not to do, and hope that the training and intelligence of his physician will make the patient's stay as short and pleasant as possible. With the experience and skill in what has been called the art of medicine, the anxieties and inconveniences of the move to the hospital may be minimized, while full advantage is taken of all that it has to offer.

Although everyone agrees to the desirability of good hospital records on private patients, they are often deplorably meager. The sketchy history and almost nonexistent progress notes deprive the record of its value as a source of information for subsequent investigation as well as for the later care of the patient. Observations that might later have proved to be of the utmost value are forever lost because they were not recorded. Although perfectly clear at the time, the memory of these variations and fluctuations in the patient's course fades rapidly. Furthermore, should the patient move or transfer to another physician, a complete history of this illness might be the most vital contribution toward elucidating a later sickness. Important as it is for others, a good hospital record is equally valuable for the doctor himself. He will learn much about his own patients that they themselves may have forgotten, if only he persists in recording his observations. How often they will deny, as soon as several months later, symptoms they complain about today! Finally, more complete records may not only save embarrassment but make the ordeal considerably easier, should the physician be called upon to testify in court.

CLINIC WORK

In return for the privileges it extends to the doctor — offering him a place for the care of his private patients, furthering his postgraduate education in a variety of ways, and helping to make him a better doctor — the hospital has the right to expect certain services. It should be clearly understood that these services are not granted as a favor, but are part of each staff member's duty. Every hospital exists primarily to serve the sick of the community, including those who do not have the means to pay for it. In some areas, particularly in industrial centers, the medically indigent may be numerous, whereas in less populated rural areas they may be few. Depending on the local need, the hospital may or may not have a "free" clinic or outpatient department for needy ambulatory patients. (The term free, although in such common use, had best be abandoned, not only because of its degrading implications, but because the service is actually no longer free.) In areas where outpatient hospital clinics are not needed, it is up to the doctors of the community to care for these needy sick themselves. It is unfortunate that attendance at outpatient clinics is so often regarded as a burden by the doctors. How much of this attitude is the result of a belief that they are offering a gratuity, and consequently need not put forth their best efforts, and how much the result of poorly run outpatient departments, is not easy to determine. Undoubtedly, both factors are partly to blame. In any case, outpatient clinics can be a rich source of clinical material, and with the co-operation of the hospital staff, can contribute greatly to the doctor's education.

The time spent in such clinics will depend entirely on the number of patients and the size of the staff. The larger the number of doctors, the less time each one will have to devote to this necessary effort. In general, the younger — and presumably less busy — doctors will be expected to spend more time in outpatient clinics than their elder brethren. On the other hand, the size of a physician's practice or the extent of his other obligations should in no way determine the amount of time he devotes to outpatient work. These are questions to be settled by each hospital staff. But once they have been settled it is absolutely essential to the success and proper running of the clinic that each doctor carry out his obligations to it conscientiously. That means regular attendance and getting to the clinic on time. There may be occasions when certain emergencies may delay or prevent him from getting there, but if this happens too frequently his usefulness to the hospital becomes seriously impaired. Furthermore, it throws an additional load on the more conscientious members of the staff. All too frequently the outpatient clinic work becomes an afterthought, to be squeezed in when, as, and if time permits.

Since one of the major tenets of the proponents of compulsory medical insurance is that it would provide more adequate care for the needy sick, it behooves us to improve this care if we wish to avoid so-called socialized medicine. Certainly outpatient clinics are one area where improvements can be made, and doctors must cease looking upon patients of these clinics as second-rate citizens.

THE HOSPITAL IN TEACHING AND RESEARCH

For the needy sick who require hospital care, most communities arrange for beds in the local hospital, or elsewhere, should specialized skill be required. The "service" ward is also the responsibility of the hospital staff, and its size will depend on the character of the area served. In some localities it may amount to no more than a few beds; in university teaching hospitals it may represent the main source of patients. The care and attention these patients receive will depend primarily on the emphasis devoted to the education of the doctor; it may vary from superb to casual. Where the emphasis is chiefly on the care of private patients, the ward service patient is less likely to receive the skilled care expected in teaching hospitals, where the more experienced members of the staff supervise his diagnosis and treatment. This should be a challenge to the more inquisitive and industrious practitioners in community hospitals away from medical centers. Better use of this clinical material will not only benefit themselves, but will be of infinite advantage to the patient and the hospital. The educational value of the entire hospital can be enormously improved by increasing the emphasis on the care of the needy ill, particularly in those institutions where private patients predominate.

Another fruitful field is the problem of obtaining autopsies. The value of post-mortem examinations would hardly seem to deserve emphasis, were it not for their lamentable infrequency in so many of our hospitals. That this glaring deficiency is exclusively the fault of the medical community is self-evident, for there is no question but that permission for such examinations would be more frequently granted if more frequently requested. The reluctance to ask for such permission is difficult to defend in view of its immense and proven value. The motives lying behind this reluctance are many and need not be enumerated here, but if the hospital is to maintain its vital function in the education of the doctor, this is a field to which the entire staff can contribute. Furthermore, they will not only help educate themselves, but the community as well.

This leads to the role of the practitioner in teaching, regardless of where he may practice. Depending on his background, special interest, training, and where he has settled, there are teaching opportunities for him wherever he may decide to utilize them. The physician in a small community who desires to teach, but finds himself bereft of medical students or a group of interns, may still find an outlet among his colleagues on the staff, via hospital meetings, organized hospital rounds, journal groups, or clinicopathological conferences. Much, of course, will depend on the willingness of his colleagues to participate. This is where a properly managed "service" ward and frequent post-mortem examinations might be the spark for such an educational program. The exact form it takes is quite immaterial, and will vary with the staff, but the opportunities are there, waiting to be grasped.

Emphasis has been placed here on the smaller hospital, since the majority of physicians will not be affiliated with teaching hospitals where such programs are already in full swing. The standards of a hospital will be directly proportional to the amount and quality of its teaching. Where there is no teaching, no eager young minds will be attracted and the general medical level will fall. Where there is no teaching, competent interns will not apply, and the hospital, which may sorely need their help, may either have to struggle along without them, or may attract a few less desirable ones by offering attractive salaries. And without the searching, probing younger medical minds, the older ones soon begin to lose their sharpness. Each side has something that will be of benefit to the other.

Every hospital, wherever it may be, can fulfill — at least in part or to some degree — its function in the education of the doctor. Some physicians are more educable than others; some are better able to educate than others. That there are many obstacles to even the most modest teaching program is readily recognized. Inertia and apathy must be overcome. Generally it will be the younger practitioners, newer to the community, who will be most likely to originate and implement any new educational or teaching plans, often to be met with hostility and negation from their medical elders. No guide can be offered how best to overcome these and other obstacles; but with tact and a will to do it, they can be surmounted. Starting perhaps in a very small way, and gradually expanding if success crowns the earlier effort, an effective teaching program can eventually be evolved.

To those with an investigative turn of mind, the hospital also offers opportunities for research, both basic and clinical. Generally speaking, it will be research on clinical problems that will appeal to the practitioner most, and that his training will have equipped him for best. There is much still to be learned about the most commonly encountered diseases — their natural history, normal variations, and unusual manifestations; careful and patient observation may cast valuable light on them. Whatever the problems, the hospital will be the chief source of the researcher's material, since his own practice is not likely to supply him with the necessary number or variety of patients. But here again it will be the service wards or outpatient clinics that will offer the most fertile field for his endeavors.

To be sure, the occasional physician in whom the spark of investigation burns brightly may find opportunities everywhere. The memory of Sir James Mackenzie, making polygraphic tracings on almost every patient, cannot readily be forgotten. Not to be forgotten either is the magnitude of his contribution to the understanding of cardiac arrythmias. But just as the polygraph gave way to the electrocardiograph — much to Sir James's annoyance — the hospital has replaced the individual research effort, and for reasons quite apparent and understandable. As stated earlier in this chapter, one of the chief functions of the hospital is to further our knowledge of disease, to promote medical research. As with teaching, this need not be solely the province of the university hospital. The community hospital also offers opportunities for research, even if on a more modest scale. They are there for the grasping.

REFERENCE

1. FAXON, N. W., editor. *The Hospital in Contemporary Life*. Cambridge: Harvard University Press, 1949.

9

Medical Organization

by Walter B. Martin

MEDICINE is not static. Neither can the practitioner of medicine remain static. However well prepared he may be on entering the profession, he will either advance or retreat from that point. If he is to grow, he must constantly strive to improve his knowledge of the science of medicine, broaden and consolidate his experience, and perfect his technic in the art of its practice. Medicine is also a social force and is played upon by other social forces. These forces will to a high degree determine the environment in which medicine is practiced, and will stimulate or retard its progress. Social and economic factors may affect medical education and research, and the production, distribution, and cost of medical care. The doctor's activities should, therefore, include participation in the social and economic fields of medicine. As his primary concern the physician must, of course, continue throughout life the program of medical education begun in his medical school. Since the frontiers of medical knowledge are constantly changing, whatever degree of education and training he may have on entering practice is only a basis for further advancement in knowledge and skill.

Medical education at the local level may be continued by study of one's own cases, by reading, and by contacts with fellow physicians in the local society and at hospital staff conferences. The most effective means of advancing one's own knowledge is in teaching others, even though in a small way. Hospital appointments may afford this opportunity. At the state and national level there are unlimited opportunities of advancement through attending special courses offered by medical societies, hospitals, and medical schools.

Experience gained is of little value unless it is recorded and compared with the experience of others. Records are necessary, not only to give one the benefit of a continuous story of a patient's troubles over a period of time, but also to help preserve one's intellectual honesty. Without records, therapeutic triumphs become magnified and the unpleasant facts of failures are dimmed or forgotten. Nothing is more stimulating, or at times perhaps more humiliating, than, on reviewing a patient's case, to have recourse to a record of years before and find to what degree the patient's problem was correctly evaluated at the time of the previous examination. Hippocrates may have had this in mind when he observed that "experience is fallacious." This is not so when experience is fortified by carefully recorded observations over a period of years.

Professional contacts with other physicians are necessary. These can be gained through hospital or clinic appointments. Such appointments should be sought early no matter how low may be the rung of the ladder on which the physician starting out in practice may find his foot. Progress from there is always possible. The stimulation of contact with other minds and of noting other methods of approach to a problem is always important.

Medical literature is so extensive that it is difficult for the practitioner to review even a small part of it, except in co-operation with others. The journal club is an effective medium for the solution of this problem. Regardless of one's special field, it is often valuable to join in a reading club not confined to a single specialty, but one that includes a number of men of varied interests. The specialist who is familiar with only his own particular segment of medicine is greatly handicapped. He should at least know the capabilities of the general men and of the specialists in the various fields, and what can be offered his patient by each of them. The reading club affords the opportunity to hear evaluations of many articles covering the different phases of medicine. One can then select for further detailed study those papers that appear to have particular merit. After having had experience in the general type of journal club, one may later choose a club limited to a special field of medicine.

With this background of recording of clinical findings, based on the study of one's own patients and of those encountered in clinics, together with a knowledge of current medical literature, one is prepared to take part in discussions of scientific subjects in the medical society and staff conferences. Exposure to the criticism and comments of others emphasizes the necessity of being able to fortify one's opinions with fact, and aids in developing some facility in speaking and writing. From there on opportunity broadens, and progress is limited only by one's devotion to the art and science of medicine and one's willingness to work. Progress in postgraduate education can continue throughout life, and can move from the local to the state and to the national level.

SPECIALTY BOARDS

Those who enter the practice of medicine come with different equipments. They may have progressed through a full residency and have completed the formal training required by the board of the specialty of their choice. Others may have had a lesser degree of training, down to a single year of internship. In some instances this has been by choice, and in others it has been a matter of necessity. Many capable students find themselves unable, even if they so desire, to complete the formal training required for admission to the examinations of one of the specialty boards. Fortunately, in this country the way remains open for them to enter practice and later qualify for board examinations. The requirements of the several boards vary. These requirements are set forth each year in the internship and residency number of the *Journal of the American Medical Association* usually published in September. The student or the young physician should review these requirements carefully so that he can plan the course that he may desire to pursue. Whatever one may think of the present rather rigid requirements of certain boards, they do, as far as the individual physician is concerned, have to a considerable degree control of his destiny.

There are at present eighteen specialty boards that have been approved by the Council on Medical Education and Hospitals of the American Medical Association and the Advisory Board for Medical Specialties, not including certain subspecialties certified by some of the specialty boards. The Advisory Board for Medical Specialties was organized in 1933 and 1934. This board is made up of two members from each of the approved medical specialty boards and two from four other organizations having a legitimate interest in the education, examination, and certification of medical specialists. These four are the Association of American Medical Colleges, the American Hospital Association, the Federation of State Medical Boards, and the National Board of Medical Examiners. Prior to the organization of the Advisory Board, certain specialty boards were already in existence and there was nothing to prevent any medical group from setting up a board in any particular field. The eighteen specialty examining and certifying boards are set up under the Council on Medical Education and Hospitals of the American Medical Association, and the Advisory Board for Medical Specialties.

The purpose of the examining boards in the specialties is to determine the competency in a certain field of candidates who present themselves for certification. These boards are also concerned with the development and evaluation of training facilities. They advise physicians regarding the proper course of study, training, and preparation for examination by the boards. Certification does not confer on anyone any special or legal qualification. It does not in any way serve to limit the practice of a nonboard member who conforms to the law of his state and considers himself competent to practice in a certain field.

Certain general qualifications are required by all boards, such as citizenship, moral and ethical standards, and active membership in local and state societies. The last requirement is waived for physicians in the federal medical services, and under certain exceptional circumstances for others. Each of the eighteen boards has its own particular requirements in terms of education, training, and experience. Information about the requirements of any one of the medical specialty boards may be obtained from the Advisory Board for Medical Specialties.

The medical student, as early as possible in his career, should become familiar with the requirements of the several boards, so as to plan his future activities accordingly. It is not necessary, and indeed not always desirable, for him to pursue his postgraduate studies through a full residency course, and thus meet the formal training requirements of the boards. There is much to be said for interrupting training after the second graduate year in order to gain experience in the practice of medicine before completing formal training. Knowledge, without the wisdom acquired from experience in the responsibility of actual practice, may at times be a detriment. Certainly an interlude of experience in practice is of great value to the student when he resumes his formal training. Provisions made by the Board of Internal Medicine, whereby these additional years in practice and special study may be substituted for certain years of more formal training, have much to commend them.

The specialty boards are: American Board of Anesthesiology, American Board of Dermatology and Syphilology, American Board of Internal Medicine, American Board of Neurological Surgery, American Board of Obstetrics and Gynecology, American Board of Ophthalmology, American Board of Orthopaedic

Surgery, American Board of Otolaryngology, American Board of Pathology, American Board of Pediatrics, American Board of Physical Medicine and Rehabilitation, American Board of Plastic Surgery, American Board of Preventive Medicine, American Board of Proctology, American Board of Psychiatry and Neurology, American Board of Radiology, American Board of Surgery, American Board of Thoracic Surgery (a subsidiary of the American Board of Surgery), and the American Board of Urology.

Two of the boards certify candidates in subspecialties if the candidate holds a certificate in the primary field. The American Board of Internal Medicine certifies in allergy, cardiovascular disease, gastroenterology, and pulmonary diseases. The American Board of Pediatrics certifies in pediatric allergy. Five boards confer certificates in special divisions. The American Board of Obstetrics and Gynecology will issue certificates in obstetrics or gynecology only; the American Board of Otolaryngology grants a limited certificate in endoscopy; the American Board of Pathology issues certificates in pathologic anatomy, clinical pathology, and other special fields of interest; the American Board of Psychiatry and Neurology in psychiatry and neurology; and the American Board of Radiology in nine special divisions, including radiology, therapeutic radiology, radium therapy, and medical nuclear physics.

General practice must always be the sound basis of good medical care in this country. At the present time, more than two-thirds of our physicians who are actively engaged in the practice of medicine are general practitioners. They are sharing to an increased extent in the available facilities for postgraduate training. Many teaching hospitals are offering two-year mixed internships, designed particularly for those who plan to enter general practice. Hospitals are also establishing sections on general practice on both an in-patient and out-patient basis. The Academy of

General Practice requires a certain number of hours per year of postgraduate training on the part of its members.

The present world situation has posed a problem for the military, the teaching hospitals, and the student alike. A young physician, after completing his first year of internship, is liable to be called for a two-year tour of duty with the armed forces. If he is not called, he can be deferred for a six-months' period only, but after this he may or may not be deferred again. This presents the hospitals with an unstable group in resident training and keeps the student in a state of jeopardy. While the program supplies the armed forces with a large group of men with only one year's training, it leaves a dearth of those needed to fill the gap between the ward officer and the chief of service. The problem of course does not present itself to those who have already discharged their military obligation, but this group is decreasing rapidly.

SOCIETIES AND ASSOCIATIONS

Men in almost every walk of life join themselves together in organizations in which they have a common interest or a common objective. Their objectives may be altruistic or selfish, or, often, a mixture of both. "Joining" has become a part of the pattern of American life. This is necessarily so in a country as large and as populous as ours. Medicine is no exception. National, state, and local medical societies abound. No physician can be insensible of their impact on medicine, nor can he stand apart from those associations that will further his purposes as a good physician. If he is to continue to advance in medical knowledge, if he is to discharge his full duty to society by aiding in the solution of the problems of medicine, he must join with others of similar interests and purposes.

The county medical society is the basic, and probably the most important, unit in medical organization and should be one of the

most useful groups in any community. Through the county society the physician becomes acquainted with his fellow practitioners and should develop awareness of the broad general medical, health, and social problems in his immediate area. If he is to
discharge his proper function as a physician, he cannot confine his
interests and activities to the field of professional activities alone.
From the local medical society he should broaden his activities
to include work in other community groups — religious, civic,
and welfare.

As already mentioned, he should early seek hospital or clinic
staff appointments and devote a suitable part of his time to non-
remunerative activities in the field of medicine. Association with
the local medical society should not be limited to joining with the
purpose of establishing his standing in medicine. He should attend the meetings and listen to the discussions, taking part in
them if informed on the subject being discussed. In his early
years, when not too much pressed for time, he should form the
habit of participating in the society work; this habit will probably
persist in later years, even though other demands crowd upon
him. The good local medical society is a focal point from which
the total health needs of a community can be observed, studied,
and evaluated. From the society should come the stimulus to the
improvement of preventive services, hospital facilities, and measures for the extension of good medical care to all of the people of
the community.

The next step in the organizational phase of medicine is the
state society. Here the broader aspects of medicine come into view
as they affect the state and often the surrounding areas. Each
county society, at an annual meeting, elects representatives to the
state society's house of delegates or council. Whereas the total
membership in a local society formulates the policy and takes
action on matters brought before it, the house of delegates of the
state society may transact its business only at its regular meetings.
During the interval between meetings of the state representative

body, the affairs of the society are controlled or managed by a board of trustees or other small group elected by the delegates. The state societies or associations also elect delegates to the House of Delegates of the American Medical Association. Each state is entitled to one representative in the national House of Delegates for each thousand members, or fraction thereof, of the state society, who are also active members of the American Medical Association.

The American Medical Association is made up of 53 state and territorial organizations. Its House of Delegates is comprised of representatives from these constituent organizations, together with representatives of each of the scientific sections of the American Medical Association, and one from each of the five major divisions of the federal medical services. The House of Delegates of the American Medical Association is the supreme policy-making body of that organization. It establishes its own rules of order and elects its speaker. It chooses the President and other elective officers of the Association, including nine members of its Board of Trustees. Members of the Board are elected for a period of five years and may not serve more than two terms. The President and President-Elect of the Association are also members of the Board of Trustees by virtue of their office, with power to vote.

The House of Delegates meets twice each year. In the interval between the meetings, the affairs of the Association are managed by the Board of Trustees. Reports of all actions taken by the Board are made at each meeting of the House of Delegates and are subject to approval or disapproval by the House. The Board of Trustees is also responsible for the management of the financial affairs of the Association.

The activities of the Association are carried out through a number of councils and bureaus. These cover such important programs as those of the Council on Medical Education and Hospitals, the Council on Medical Service, the Council on Rural

Health, the Council on Industrial Health, the Council on Food and Nutrition, the Council on Pharmacy and Chemistry, the Bureau of Legal Medicine, the Bureau of Medical Economic Research, the Bureau of Health Education, and many other activities having an important bearing on the health and welfare of the American people.

In spite of the size and complexity of the national organization, an avenue is open for obtaining action or a declaration of policy on any matter originating in a local society. A resolution passed by a local organization goes to the state society, and if approved, may be presented to the national House of Delegates. Any delegate may also introduce a resolution on his own initiative, or one sponsored by a group of delegates. All resolutions are referred to reference committees of the House, appointed by the speaker. These reference committees hold hearings and report their findings and recommendations to the House. This body may approve, disapprove, or amend any report of a reference committee. Any member of the American Medical Association may appear and testify before any reference committee. Other persons having a special interest in a particular subject may be requested or permitted to testify at a hearing of these committees. It is possible, therefore, for individual local societies or state societies to have a voice in influencing the policy and of directing the affairs of the American Medical Association. The basic policy of the Association is set forth in its constitution, which declares its purpose to be "the advancement of the art and the science of medicine and the betterment of the public health." It promotes this objective through the activities of its various councils and bureaus, its scientific assembly, the *Journal of the American Medical Association,* and its nine special journals. Through the Committee on Legislation and the Washington office of the Association, physicians are kept informed of proposed or pending legislation in the field of health.

These bills are numerous and may be important in their relation to medicine and the medical care and welfare of the people. Whatever one's view may be regarding these many bills, a knowledge of their content is important, since they may affect for good or evil the future development of medicine, and the quantity, quality, and availability of medical care.

Medicine has many facets. Its base is fundamental research in every field of science. From this grows more specific research pertaining to its particular problems. Next is the teaching of scientific medicine, making use of all the accumulated knowledge and experience of the past. But medicine is also a healing art, and the effective application of medical knowledge to the prevention and cure of disease involves a sympathetic understanding of people, of their environment, their problems as individuals, and their way of life. Medicine also involves an understanding of the social and economic factors concerned in the production, the cost, and the distribution of medical care. It follows, then, that the continued activities of the physician must touch on many fields if he is to discharge his true mission of advancing the art and science of medicine and bettering the public health.

SERVICES OF THE AMERICAN MEDICAL ASSOCIATION

A physician in good standing in the constituent medical association of the state or territory in which he practices may enroll as a member of the American Medical Association on payment of dues. As a dues-paying member, he can receive without further payment the *Journal of the American Medical Association* or any one of the nine specialty journals published by the Association. In addition, he can make use of any of the many councils, committees, and bureaus established within the framework of the Association.

The Directory Department develops and publishes at intervals biographical information on physicians in the United States, its dependencies, and Canada. From the Directory as from the Department inquiring physicians can learn the addresses of former colleagues and obtain other data. From the Council on Medical Education and Hospitals facts are available on medical schools and hospitals, internships and residencies, technical schools, postgraduate courses, and medical licensure.

Members may make application to present papers or exhibits at the annual meetings of the Association. They may call for the loan of films from the Committee on Medical Motion Pictures, for the loan of medical journals and reprints from the Library, for information on drugs and treatment from the Council on Pharmacy and Chemistry, for data on foods and devices from the Council on Foods and Nutrition and the Council on Physical Medicine and Rehabilitation, and for facts on quacks and fads from the Bureau of Investigation. From the Committee on Legislation an appraisal of medical bills offered to the Congress is available, and from the Bureau of Medical Economic Research, costs of medical care, distribution of physicians, and other socioeconomic data of interest.

The Council on Medical Service offers information on insurance plans, group practice, medical care programs, and opportunities for practice. The Bureau of Health Education has available material for the preparation of speeches, particularly for lay groups, and pamphlets on many subjects in the field of health education. From the Bureau of Legal Medicine and Legislation can be obtained information on medicolegal and legislative subjects. The Bureau usually can be helpful to the inquiring physician who is faced with a medicolegal question, but it cannot, of course, serve as the physician's attorney.

Other offices provide other services, an index to which can be found in the booklets *Guide to Services* and *It's Your A.M.A.,* both of which can be obtained on request from the American Medical Association, 535 North Dearborn St., Chicago 10, Illinois. The Association can help the individual physician by answering his questions, but it serves in other ways as well. It aids in the improvement of drugs, it helps raise the standards for hospitals and medical schools, it watches over federal legislation of medical significance, it explores medical care problems, and it examines the problems pertaining to service in the armed forces. But it does more than this. For example, it works closely with many other organizations of a national or more localized character. Its broad coverage can be appreciated only when the physician tests its value to him by examining closely what it does for him, for the profession and for the public. To meet this test, the Association employs almost 900 people, including more than 30 physicians, 10 doctors of philosophy, and several attorneys!

There are each year several special issues of the *Journal of the American Medical Association*. In May there is published what is known as the Hospital Number, in the same month the State Board Number, in June and December the Postgraduate and Continuation Courses numbers, in September the Education and the Internship and Residency numbers. These special issues provide information on topics that concern all medical students and graduates. From time to time those in practice will be specially interested in postgraduate courses and the specialty boards.

10

Community Medical Resources

by Henry F. Howe

O<small>NCE HE HAS CHOSEN HIS</small> location and type of practice, set up and equipped his office, and established his hospital and medical society affiliations, the physician may think his preparations for a lifelong practice are complete. Actually they have just begun. The general has a headquarters, a command, and a mission, but all his tactical planning for the campaign still lies ahead of him.

Among other things his practice promptly presents him with countless needs for learning legal and quasi-official technics that were taken care of for him while he was still an intern. He is required to make out not only birth certificates and death certificates, but serological reports for marriage and pregnancy; he fills out contagious disease reports, proofs of death, accident and health insurance forms, Blue Shield applications, and many varieties of physical examination blanks for insurance or employment. He certifies illness of employees, vaccinations of school children, and gunshot wounds for the police. He must learn which deaths to refer to the medical examiner or coroner, which charity cases to the public welfare board or Veterans' Administration, which child or senile patients to aid to dependent children or old age assistance. There are industrial accident reports to send in, venereal disease regulations to comply with, and committals of the insane to process. He gradually learns that he must keep on his shelves up-to-date copies of the manuals of procedure of the state department of health, the Veterans' Administration, and Blue Shield. He must know the State Department's requirements for immunizations of travelers to foreign countries. He learns where to refer sick military personnel, and how to refer parents to a good adoption agency.

Modern civilization, and especially modern government, have filled the physician's life with the irritating details of such paper work. The fact should not be lost sight of, however, that these time-consuming technics often place in the hands of the physician adequate tools for the disposal of difficult patient problems that were not available to him a generation ago. They enable him to handle a volume of social problems that he could not have encompassed by the hit-or-miss methods of the good old days. Many of these forms and blanks represent easy solutions, through government or insurance, of problems that the unaided physician used to take care of inadequately through charities that he often had to dream up himself or supply from poor community resources. They have removed, by this red tape process, a considerable share for the burden of improvisation that the physician formerly bore in caring for the poor.

Others of these technics are actually those of preventive medicine. The immunizations, industrial accidents, venereal and contagious disease procedures, and compulsory serological tests, fall in this category. Police, psychiatric, and medicolegal technics, in so far as they serve the public safety, are likewise in the broadest sense preventive medicine.

Different states and communities vary widely in the degree of development and methods of handling of such administrative matters. There is therefore nothing to be gained here by going into detail about procedure. It is, however, of the utmost importance for the physician to make his own study of all available community resources in his particular area, in order to familiarize himself with the procedures required by each agency. His secretary should be trained to take much of the detailed paper work off his shoulders as time goes on, but the doctor himself must thoroughly understand the methods involved. These are tools of his profession as surely as the drugs and instruments in his office. The public will measure him as shrewdly by his ready use of these tools as by his handling of disease. Insurance, employment, and public safety are all a part of the medical problem from the patient's viewpoint. The family of the insane, the aged, the worker in industry, or the chronically ill judge their physician as much by his adeptness in handling the economic factor as by his clinical judgment. His expression of annoyance at filling out a paper is interpreted as lack of interest in their problem.

If this is true of the mere matter of paper work, how much more is it true of his use of the more individualized social and professional agencies of his particular region. Most communities have their own special arrangements about ambulance service, oxygen therapy, state-supplied vaccines, pregnancy and Rh-factor tests, hearing aid and remedial reading clinics, and chest X-ray services. Some of these may be afforded very simply by the hospital. But if not, then it is the physician's responsibility to know how to obtain them with most consideration for the patient's pocketbook. Needy patients should not be denied such services if they are obtainable through public funds or private charitable agencies. People of moderate means should not be sent to an expensive source if a competent, inexpensive one is ethically available. Such full information is part of the physician's equipment. No one forgives him for hiring a private ambulance if a good police ambulance is available to every citizen.

By the same token, it is important for the doctor to have accurate information about the proper use of both public and private agencies for the diagnosis and care of chronic illness. In the fields of tuberculosis, cancer, diabetes, arthritis, heart disease, poliomyelitis, and rehabilitation there now exist public or endowed foundations in many states for cushioning the economic disaster of these prolonged disabilities. There are few people

nowadays so prosperous as not to need such help. It has become
part of the doctor's function to co-operate with these organizations in the referral and follow-up care of such cases. It is short-
sighted to allow a family to spend itself into bankruptcy in
private care of such situations where adequate facilities are
available at less cost. When people are put out of action in the
combat of life, a good chain of evacuation affords the only
chance for a patient to live to fight another day. Piling complete
economic catastrophe on top of partial physical disaster often
allows little on which to build later rehabilitation. The medical
practitioner sometimes holds this choice in his hands in his manner of disposal of prolonged illness. The large teaching hospital in
which the young physician was trained had social workers whose
career was spent in the study and policy determination of such
problems. In private practice the physician is often necessarily
his own social worker.

The same principle applies to the use of convalescent and
nursing homes as contrasted with hospital care and with special
nursing in the home. A physician should inspect the convalescent
and nursing homes in his region, know the competence of their
nursing staffs, and how to allocate patients to them with some
regard to the kind of care they are going to get in each. Similarly he should learn all he can about the availability of good
household or partially trained nurses for home care of disabled or
aged patients. His hospital he necessarily knows, but he should
be in possession of firsthand knowledge about the available alternatives to hospital care in chronic illness. Where can the
hemiplegic patient get really rehabilitating care? Where can the
patient with an orthopedic problem get physiotherapy? At what
point must the senile person be committed to a psychiatric ward?
Where can the patient with terminal cancer most happily live
out her last days?

Consideration should be given to the choice and use of nurses.
Certain physicians get a bad reputation among nurses, usually

for attaching blame to them where it is undeserved. Either the physician is so vague in giving orders that whatever the nurse does turns out to be wrong, or he is so rigid in his requirements that the nurse is afraid to adapt the orders to the real situation. Every physician should regard the nurse as a member of an allied profession that has its own standards of conduct and procedure, beyond which she cannot be expected to go. He cannot fairly ask her to diagnose disease or to carry out treatment without specific orders. So-called standing orders are of very doubtful validity unless the doctor periodically checks the patient and confirms such orders to the nurse. Yet because of her watchfulness the nurse's judgment about alarming or unusual symptoms can be of very great help to the physician, and her warning in their incipience often saves him from the embarrassment of overlooking serious complications. A doctor who closes his ears to such suggestions or brushes them off impatiently is not making full use of his resources. The skillful physician learns to evaluate the individual capacities of his nurses and apply personnel management principles to the placement, especially for private duty, of certain nurses in certain types of cases, or in certain personality problems among his patients. No medicine or regime of treatment can approach in effectiveness the proper choice of the right nurse for the particular patient in these cases. And nothing can ensure the continuity of such effective relations so much as expressions of appreciation of the nurse where her work deserves it. By the same token, she should not be reprimanded in the patient's presence any more than one would reprimand another physician in the same circumstances. Good care of the patient requires the feeling of confidence that only mutual courtesy can provide.

It is advisable for any physician to keep a list or card file of nurses for special assignments in private duty. He may thus succeed better in prescribing the nurse to meet a given need. This is particularly desirable among partly trained nurses or attendant or practical nurses, where the degree of education and experience is so variable as to be undetermined except through previous experience. The degree of rehabilitation in prolonged or chronic illness sometimes almost wholly depends on the ability of the physician to choose an intelligent willing attendant and train her on the job. In obtaining such invaluable service, a card index in the doctor's own office can be a more fruitful resource than a nurses' registry, although the registries themselves usually make excellent assignments.

The problem of the use of community resources is in essence the problem of referral. Thus far we have discussed chiefly the institutional and public agency types of referrals. No discussion of community resources could be complete, however, without some attention to the choice of medical referrals, or consultations. To some this may seem superfluous, since all practitioners build up for themselves a group of specialist consultants of their own choosing, often for quite personal reasons. But if the study of therapeutics is a lifelong one, so also should be the study of consultation. The sending of a patient to a consultant often has quite as momentous significance in the history of an illness as the choice of a drug or of any other treatment. And the availability of good consultants in many fields is a community problem. So also is the manner of consultation.

In group medicine and in hospital practice certain almost inevitable limitations arise in the choice of consultant specialists. A pseudo-business device, the "interdepartmental communication," becomes a habit, and if the staff is big enough, there is still a fairly good selection of men to choose from. But in smaller staffs this device may produce a strict limitation of choice of consultant.

In individual practice the case may be quite different. The physician may, if he wishes, play the field. He has the whole community or region to choose from. He should try to choose consultants so good that their testimony will stand up well in court. He should also pay attention to the technics of consultation. Instead of a consultation request on a hospital record sheet on which the consultant writes his opinion, the referring doctor more often sends the patient to the office of the chosen consultant. This is a new relationship. There are several ways of handling it. He can call up the consultant on the telephone, make the appointment, and send the patient along. He can write a few lines on a prescription blank. He can write a letter. Among those choices may lie the effectiveness, or lack of it, of the consultation, and there should be a clear understanding between the two physicians as to what is wanted.

Does the referring physician want a diagnosis, or an opinion, or treatment, or moral support? Does he in sending the patient expect the consultant to take over care of the illness? Does he need a definite commitment whether the patient should change his job or go South for the winter? Just what is the question? Should the consultant tell the patient the diagnosis, or is that for the referring physician's ear only? Is the patient supposed to report back to the consultant, or to the referring doctor? Is an insurance question involved? Who should order further studies or X rays?

Vagueness, both in the requesting and in the answering of such questions, is responsible for many misunderstandings among physicians and their patients. Without a letter or definite notes made at the time of a telephone conversation, many such consultations go astray, aim wide of their mark, and make the patient feel he has spent a specialist fee for nothing. The fault is often twofold, consisting of a lack of method on the part of the physician and his consultant. But the failure of method is not a medical failure so much as it is an administrative one. If a consultation is needed, it is worth doing well. Some physicians use a blank form on which the pertinent questions are checked off, with space left for the answers. This may seem coldly efficient, but it is effective.

It is by now obvious that many of the problems of wise use

of community resources in the practice of medicine are administrative ones. As our American society matures, these medical administrative functions in the community tend more and more to become organized in certain patterns of control; these may conveniently be grouped in two broad categories. The first category is voluntarily controlled, and includes the professional activities of doctors, nurses, and hospitals, the administration of medical facilities in industry and voluntary insurance, and the charitable medical resources of medical foundations, endowed clinics, and public charities. The second great category is that of government health resources, and this of course divides itself naturally into municipal, county, state and federal agencies.

In this chapter we are not concerned with the political implications of the broad division of health agencies into voluntary versus governmental control. We are dealing here only with the reality as it exists. The physician has to work with both types of agencies, and his only concern is the most effective care of the patient by wise use of all resources available, whatever their origin. It is no service to the patient to deny him the advantage of facilities routinely provided by government or industry if these services are ethically administered.

Partly through pressure from insurance companies and partly because of employers' liability laws, most large industries, banks, and commercial houses now maintain medical departments. The trend is spreading rapidly into smaller industries, where facilities for at least part-time coverage by physicians and nurses are becoming common. There are many opportunities in this field for young physicians. But whether or not a doctor actually draws a retainer from a business organization for part-time or full-time services in industry, he will inevitably treat some industrial cases. It is of the utmost importance that he understand the point of view of industrial or occupational medicine. *The chief concern of industry is the prevention of lost time from the job.* The injury or illness of skilled workers often seriously retards or stops production and increases insurance costs, as well as suspending the income of workers' families. The job of industrial physicians and nurses is not primarily the care of industrial accidents, but rather the prompt return of the worker to useful employment. Therefore when the private practitioner is dealing with an industrial case, it behooves him to co-operate with this occupational purpose for the good of all concerned. Unnecessarily prolonged convalescence serves no useful purpose. And if during convalescence the attending physician will inquire of the company doctor or nurse whether part-time or light work is available for his patient, he will usually earn the gratitude of both the patient and the company doctor. It goes without saying that he should render prompt reports on his patient's progress when these are requested by the company medical department. The industrial clinic is in a sense another community resource that can be used for the better care of the patient if only it is realized that the patient's job is one of the tools of medical care. Rehabilitation is not confined to amputees, but includes every cardiac, neurotic, or peptic ulcer patient who loses time from work because of illness. Most industrial physicians welcome the co-operation of the attending physician in early placement of such cases on part-time or light work as one of the methods of convalescent care. A simple telephone call will usually accomplish this. The industrial clinic should be regarded as a stronghold of medical thinking within the productive jungle of industry. The industrial physician speaks the same language as the attending physician. It is easier to talk to him than to the employer.

The health resources of government are for the most part concerned with public health and public safety. Their demands on the physician in private practice are often those of official duty rather than the immediate care of a patient. The board of health is concerned with sanitation, with reports of communicable diseases, testing water and milk supplies, and the supervision of food handlers and restaurants. With the co-operation of the school physician, it enforces quarantine, attempts to control epidemics, and fosters immunizations. School and public health nurses furnish health education, social welfare technics, and *post partum* and child welfare projects. Municipal social workers in many communities handle the disposition of health problems in tuberculosis, old age, and illegitimacy. The police and courts enter the health field in alcoholism, sex offenses, and insanity as well as crime. Through coroners, medical examiners, and the district attorney, they deal with the medical problems of sudden or violent death. Every physician should know which deaths to report immediately to the medical examiner. Nowadays the local civil defense organization calls on physicians for medical planning and participation in preparation for disaster or enemy attack. These are only samples of the governmental health agencies at the municipal level with which all physicians sooner or later deal. It should be part of the setting up of a practice by any physician to go to the offices of these agencies, learn what procedures are required, and in what ways agency and physician can be of mutual service. For not only does the board of health demand reporting of contagious diseases; it also often furnishes vaccines. Not only do the police require reporting of certain offenses; they often supply oxygen, crutches, and ambulance service in emergency. Not only does the town or city clerk insist on birth registrations; in many municipalities he pays for them. Usually the physician must register with him before opening an office. The physician needs to know when he can call on the district nurse, the social worker, or the veterans' committee chairman. He must make himself acquainted with the procedures of the welfare department in obtaining municipal aid.

At the county level, it is wise to be familiar with district and superior court and grand jury routines. Someday the physician will be called on to testify. County tuberculosis sanatoria are available in some states; these should be visited and the requirements for admission studied. They often provide the best diagnostic facilities in the region. If there is a county health officer or a health or diagnostic center, these facilities need to be studied.

The state department of health often provides very complete diagnostic or bacteriological laboratory service. It frequently supplies unusual vaccines or other immunization services or equipment. While it requires venereal disease reports, it also supplies serological and bacteriological tubes or culture media. The requirements for admission to state cancer and psychiatric hospitals should be learned. Many state laws demand specific duties of physicians, and a compendium of these should be acquired from the state capitol for ready reference. This is particularly true of regulations for the registration of physicians, which in some states must be renewed periodically. State agencies often supply special services for veterans, dependent children, the aged, the blind, or the crippled. There are state-aided rehabilitation centers, mental health clinics, industrial accident boards and clinics, schools for retarded children, clinics for alcoholism, and employment services for the handicapped. Many of these services are obtainable through municipal application by the town or city welfare department or social worker, and this is usually the best source of information about them. But the local representative in the state legislature is often a good medium of inquiry if others fail. The physician should make his acquaintance in any case.

Federal agencies in the field of health are in a process of growth and transition so rapid that it is difficult to keep up with them. For this reason only the most general statements can here be made about them. As they apply to the private practice of medicine, they group themselves chiefly about the United States Public Health Service, the Veterans' Administration and the armed forces. Reference has already been made to immunization requirements of the State Department for foreign travel. The Public Health Service similarly affords vaccines for certain tropical diseases like yellow fever, usually through a government hospital in each geographical region. Its staff is available for special studies in widespread epidemics, and the practicing physician may occasionally need consultation or require information from the Public Health Service in diagnostic or sanitation problems in this field. Many federal agencies publish informational and educational pamphlets on such subjects as maternal and child health, industrial hazards, and food and drug problems. The American Medical Association, through its Chicago offices, can often provide the best information on how to secure federal government materials and services on such special problems.

By far the greatest number of problems involving federal services arise in relation to the armed forces and the Veterans' Administration. Members of the armed forces who are injured or taken sick while on leave are subject to special regulations that every physician sooner or later must know. In general, an immediate report on the man involved must be made to the commanding officer, often through the local Red Cross chapter, and usually prompt transfer to an armed forces hospital must be made unless special permission is obtained from the military unit concerned. Military discipline and the responsibility of government are as serious factors in the situation as the disease, and the private physician really has no alternative, since the military patient is not in the position of a private contractor in hiring a physician. The physician should therefore at least learn what military hospitals are available in the region and how to contact them when he needs to refer a patient. Usually these hospitals supply their own ambulance service. Often they afford facilities for the hospitalization of the families of servicemen as well as of the men themselves. It is not good medical practice to charge expenses of private hospitalization to the family of an overseas soldier when a nearby army hospital would have provided the same services free. Of course exceptions to this principle exist among the well-to-do, but the principle holds in most cases.

The care of war veterans is an even more difficult problem.

At present writing, the office care of veterans can be supervised by private-contract physicians who have been approved by the Veterans' Administration. Monthly reports and renewals of authorization to continue the care of each individual veteran are required, and the regional Veterans' Administration medical clinic usually also sees the patient periodically for review of his need for further care. If the disability is service-connected the procedure remains relatively simple, but when disabilities of non-service-connected origin become enmeshed in the problem, matters of ethics and of responsibility for the care of the patient sometimes become confused. The patient may become a segmented case, with 30 per cent of him, representing the officially estimated disability, belonging to Veterans' Administration care, 70 per cent, not service-connected, belonging theoretically to the other medical resources of the community. Hospitalization in a Veterans' Administration hospital almost inevitably occurs in non-service-connected cases under such conditions, with or without real economic need for government subsidy of the patient. Only careful individualization of each case can justify fair decisions. The private physician has no formulas to follow, and must depend on individual judgment to guide him in advising the patient how to make proper use of the facilities offered by the Veterans' Administration. The physician needs to know his community veterans' committee, and should also consult sometimes with committees of the local veterans' organizations on special problems involving a patient. Local community agencies are often the only ones that can properly be used to study the needs of veterans with particularly difficult medical problems. Under present conditions there is no effective liaison between Veterans' Administration hospitals and the family physician of the veteran. Such liaison often needs to be improvised with whatever means come to hand at both hospital and community levels.

This chapter opened with an analogy of the physician to a

general laying his tactical plans for a campaign in the field. His organization for that campaign, as we have seen, involves not only planning, but also intelligence, training, and supply. He must equip himself and his office with information about the resources available. He must utilize trained personnel, whether nurses or physicians, in the most effective way and even train certain of them for particular functions. He must consider various segments of his community — laboratories, nursing homes, and social agencies — as echelons in reserve for special supply problems. He must write clear orders, keep adequate personnel records, and render progress reports. Above all he must be prepared to call on the social and economic equipment of the community without delay or needless effort.

11

Reading and Writing

by Robert W. Buck

ALTHOUGH IT WOULD BE UNFAIR to say that a majority of practitioners make little effort to keep themselves up to date by regular or systematic reading, there are nevertheless many men in general practice and no doubt not a few who are qualified as specialists whose reading is, to say the least, desultory. In recent years the larger pharmaceutical houses have made serious and admirable attempts to supply the practitioner with abstracts of medical papers, by no means all of them selected mainly with a view to increasing the use of the products they manufacture. Such abstracts together with other advertising and promotional literature constitute, it is to be feared, a large part of the reading of many physicians. Certain of the digest journals, admirable in their way and reasonably well edited, may be added to these sources. If a smattering of information and an occasional bit of practical or technical procedure is what is desired, perhaps this is as good a method as any of obtaining it.

No practitioner, recently graduated from a first-class teaching hospital where he has been exposed to daily ward rounds at the heels of chiefs of services who are real leaders in their fields, will have difficulty in recalling at least one such medical authority who always seemed to him to have the literature of his special field at the tip of his tongue. Such a one could deliver a ten- or fifteen-minute lecture on some comparatively abstruse aspect of the medical or surgical condition under discussion, supported by references to the current literature of the subject. Erudition of this sort is not the result of desultory reading, however. It is generally a by-product of reading that has been carried on in connection with original investigation.

This gives a hint of the method by which a physician may maintain regular and profitable habits of reading. Reading for its own sake is apt to be sterile. When it is done with the purpose of enabling a man to carry on an original project with full knowledge of what has been done in the past, the information sticks because it is immediately applied to the matter in hand. A resolution to keep well informed, when not fortified by the need to do so as the result of some special interest, is made only to be broken.

Every physician beginning practice is familiar with this advice to develop and maintain an interest in a special field, but not infrequently it is difficult for him to find a subject to which he really desires to devote his attention. Nevertheless, no medical man, however scanty his experience in actual investigative work or how limited the opportunities of his practice, need feel that he is denied the opportunity for original observation. His first step, if he wishes to maintain good reading habits, is to look about him and find something within his own experience that requires further investigation and elucidation. "To observe and record for mankind" has throughout the centuries been the underlying motive for all medical progress.

BOOKS AND PERIODICALS

The number of books and periodicals required by a physician in connection with investigative and teaching activities far exceeds the capacity of any private library. For this purpose a home medical library is no more feasible than a home research laboratory. In his own medical library the practitioner requires in the way of books only a few selected volumes for ready reference, and as for journals, one or two general periodicals with a national or international circulation. Among these would certainly be the *Journal of the American Medical Association*. One or two general journals might supplement the list, in addition to which every physician will probably also receive his state medical journal and one or several specialty journals that cover the fields in which he is particularly interested.

Books

The natural interest of the physician in the history of medicine or of his specialty may be trusted to guide him in the purchase of monographs or books that will have permanent value to him and to others of similar interests. The same is true of monumental contributions that have been made in his own field. The library of an Osler, a Cushing, or a Pratt is valuable because of its content of this sort of book, often enhanced because many of the individual volumes have personal association.

In addition, reference volumes such as directories, dictionaries, and handbooks of laboratory or technical procedure are essential tools. Beyond this, a word of caution is desirable. Perhaps the best guiding principle is that books should be selected for their cultural value rather than as sources of current information. In general, textbooks are written for undergraduate students. They tend to become obsolete quickly. Few if any encyclopedic handbooks of the type that were compiled in Germany before World War I are being produced at the present time. There are no rules by which one may be guided in the selection of books that will prove to possess true scientific, historic or literary value.

Periodicals

Although most physicians subscribe to three or four or half a dozen periodicals, it is in general futile for them to attempt to save and bind them. Medical libraries do this much more completely. It is probably enough for a man to save perhaps a run of two years — the current year and the preceding one — disposing of all back numbers and making no attempt to save them. They can only become a burden to his bookshelves or to his attic.

But a wide acquaintance with periodical literature is the only means of keeping up with what is going on in the profession. For this reason it should be an obligation of every physician to see to it that there exists in his own community some sort of medical library. Whether this is associated with a medical society, a hospital, or a medical school makes little difference so long as it is provided with as wide a selection and as complete a file of current periodicals as can be afforded.

FILING AND INDEXING

The habit of filing and indexing material for future reference seems to be an inborn characteristic of some persons. It can be cultivated in others. Whether or not it is a valuable habit depends, of course, upon the nature and quality of the material that is filed and indexed. However, even material of very excellent quality, if it is collected and filed as the result of a constitutional tendency to orderliness, is not valuable unless it has been gathered in accordance with some principle of selectivity.

It is probably true that most physicians keep a scrapbook or a file of clippings and notes of general interest, usually in regard to matters of practical procedure, which they hope to use at some future date. What a man does with such odds and ends is of no great importance.

If a man has special interests, he will collect reprints of articles by his colleagues, clippings from magazines and medical journals, pamphlets, and a variety of other material; these he will put away in folders or envelopes indexed for future reference. The value of such a file depends entirely upon the capacity of the individual to select material of permanent worth. Few physicians are able to carry throughout a lifetime of practice even such elementary habits as listing and indexing the diagnoses they have made or the therapeutic procedures they have prescribed or practiced.

One difficulty here is that medical progress renders many diagnoses and procedures obsolete, or divides them into categories that were nonexistent when the file was originally established. Thus a file of cases of "acute indigestion" made in 1916 would have to be reclassified in the light of the interpretation of that diagnosis made possible by medical progress in the last forty years. At present there would be no place for such a term.

ABSTRACTS OF MEDICAL LITERATURE

The man who reads for information only is apt to be annoyed by bibliographical references. The man who reads in order to widen his acquaintance with the background of a field in which he is actively working welcomes an abundance of bibliographical material and finds a well-selected but not necessarily lengthy bibliography to be one of his criteria of the value of a published paper.

Since a good list of bibliographical references has become the hallmark of a first-rate paper, the writers of second-rate contributions find it necessary to append an imposing list of titles at the end of their articles. Nothing is more annoying to the careful student than to read what looks like a fairly good paper supplemented with an imposing bibliography, only to find that the articles and references cited bear no immediate relation to the content of the paper. Such a bibliography has probably been compiled by a secretary who has been sent to the library to make out a list of titles that seem to bear on the subject in question, or perhaps it has been provided by "lifting" sections of bibliographies taken from other papers dealing with the same general topic. There are also abstracting services which, on receipt of a request to "look up the literature" on a certain subject, will for a fee supply the inquirer with a list of titles.

The only proper way for the physician to compile a bibliography is to abstract on suitable reference cards every article that he considers of special interest or of value in his work. Each abstract card should contain the title of the article, the name of its author, and the name and date of the publication containing it, with page references. Such an abstract file is necessary to anyone who does much writing.

However, not all literature is abstracted with the single purpose of compiling a bibliography. Abstracts of the literature are a means of keeping up one's current information in any field. If such a file of abstracts is properly classified and indexed, it will be a convenience that will repay the compiler many times over for the amount of energy and time he has spent in putting it together. In general, the physician's own abstracts are preferable to those he obtains from the printed abstract columns that form a section of most medical journals. However, the latter are convenient for reviewing a field with which the student is not personally familiar. By reviewing the abstracts, a man can often gain some acquaintance with what he is unable to obtain in the original.

USE OF HOSPITAL OR MEDICAL LIBRARY FACILITIES

It is excellent practice to spend one afternoon a week, when such time is available, in the library of a hospital or other medical library with adequate facilities, reading and abstracting the current periodical literature. If this is done systematically in selected fields, the physician may acquire a comprehensive reference library of abstracts that will be invaluable to him as well as confirm his habits of reading.

Only practice will guide an investigator in securing information concerning a subject that he wishes to learn about, but there are a few fundamental procedures that must be known to anyone who expects to use intelligently the facilities of a good library.

Suppose that in your reading you run across a reference to the report of the Committee on Costs of Medical Care. You do not know what this committee was and you have only a vague idea of when it functioned. Further references suggest that it may have been a committee sponsored by the American Medical Association. Therefore, as your initial attempt to find out more about it, you consult the index numbers of the bound copies of the journals of the American Medical Association of about the era you think appropriate. You find references to a number of articles and on reading them discover that the report of the committee was published in October, 1932.

This suggests that, as a published item, it might be contained in the general catalogue of the library. You then consult this catalogue and find that there is, indeed, a published volume entitled "Final Report of the Committee on the Costs of Medical Care, 1932" and are able to obtain it by noting the library call number. This is a simple procedure.

If, however, you have only a specific subject or bit of research in mind that you wish to trace to its source, and you have no reason to connect it with any journal or society, you may then look through such comprehensive chronological indexes as the *Index Catalogue of the Surgeon General's Library,* the *Quarterly Cumulative Index Medicus,* which has been conducted for many years by the American Medical Association, or the currently valuable *Current List of Medical Literature,* published by the Armed Forces Medical Library.

By patiently studying these indexes you will find at least a few references to articles dealing with the subject in question, and you will hope that at least one of them contains an adequate bibliography. If the bibliographical data is accurate, you need then only copy it down and find out if the library has a complete file of the periodical in which the article originally appeared.

These are the elementary conveniences that the researcher must become acquainted with — the index numbers of periodicals, the indexes to periodical literature, and the card catalogue of the library. Observing previous inadequacies in the compilation of bibliographies is one of the best ways for the medical man to convince himself of the necessity of keeping records of his own references accurate and in order.

WRITING PAPERS

A physician who writes, other things being equal, is a better doctor than one who does not. This does not refer to belles-lettres (at which a good number of indifferent and a few excellent practitioners have succeeded) but to medical writing in the course of professional activity. Writing is incumbent upon the man with special training and experience as a means of making his knowledge or discoveries available to a wide audience. It is desirable for others as a means of self-education. Dr. Richard Cabot used to say that he had found no better way to familiarize himself with a subject of which he knew very little than to write a book or a paper about it.

There is no lack of opportunity for a medical man to write and to be heard, for there are almost innumerable local medical clubs, hospital staffs, and other groups, large and small, that are always ready to listen to a sincerely written paper based on original observation and experience.

Physicians have also learned that medical authorship enhances reputation and that a legitimate form of advertising their ability is to publish articles in the medical journals. This is not a reprehensible or undesirable practice, for a poorly written, unscientific, or even dishonest paper, even if it is printed by a reputable journal (which is unlikely), will in the long run serve only to mark a man for what he is.

Even though there seems to be a spate of medical writing at the present time, it is not at all certain that we write as well as our grandfathers. Anyone who has had the opportunity to study old diaries, letters, or even the minutes of society meetings, carefully and legibly handwritten in the days before typewriters became common, must have been impressed with the effort that was taken to make these records clear and intelligible to the reader. Most of them must have been written with no thought of publication, but demonstrate that when sufficient time and pains are taken to think through a subject before committing it to paper, the result will probably be a record of permanent interest and value.

I have seen notes of medical school lectures and of the remarks of a visiting physician during ward rounds, carefully recorded by conscientious and industrious medical students, that retain a value fifty or sixty years after being written that is much greater than the students realized at the time they wrote them. The practice of committing to paper almost any carefully thought-out idea or observation is highly to be commended, not only for the benefit of the person who writes and for his audience, but perhaps even for posterity.

12

Laboratory Facilities

by Donnell W. Boardman

THE TRANSITION from house officer to practicing physician is a monumental and a rude one. Not the least significant hazard of this transition is the changed relation of the clinical laboratory to the doctor. The house officer has taken for granted the battery of tests available in a teaching hospital laboratory, resting comfortably on the support that their accessibility, reliability, interpretation and relative freedom from economic pressures provide. He has had no concern in the maintenance of the laboratory, its equipment, reagents, personnel, technics, and morale, or its rapport with the clinicians it serves. All this is another's responsibility till the physician ventures into practice for himself. Whether a solo practitioner or a member of a small practicing group, the clinician must be thoroughly familiar with the workings of the clinical laboratory which serves him, if he is to make proper use and evaluation of the determinations it reports.

To establish even the most elementary of office laboratories is no mean undertaking. The employment of a single part-time technician introduces a major complication to the problems of space, repertoire, and acceptance by patients of a service that has been too long and too widely neglected in private practice. These problems and those mentioned earlier will be discussed briefly here. The tests themselves, their uses, limitations and pitfalls have been adequately presented elsewhere (1, 2, 3).

PHYSICAL LAYOUT

The laboratory need not be large if it is well planned, the existing floor space necessarily dictating its size. It will need a sink, and adequate lighting, ventilation, and work space; enough room for the technician or doctor, the patient and a companion, and it must provide a modicum of privacy from other waiting patients. Ready access to a lavatory and a couch are also mandatory.

Artificial lighting has the advantage of constancy, important in colorimetric work. Fluorescent lamps will offset their initial cost by economy of operation. They should be situated over the work space rather than in the middle of the room. Strategically placed electrical outlets will be necessary for the microscope substage lamp, centrifuge, photoelectric cell, hot plate, and refrigerator. If they are located waist high or immediately above the work space, needless bending will be obviated.

Whereas a window with a view has esthetic advantages, it may be inefficient in removing noxious odors, obligate companion to many examinations. Forced ventilation may prove a necessity, though a simple ceiling or wall vent may be sufficient for free circulation of air.

WORK SPACE

Laboratory work necessitates much getting up and sitting down. Counter-type work space is therefore desirable, at a level of about 36 inches from the floor, the sink's rim at the same level, and a high stool available for sitting up to the counter.

The sink need not be large, but a flat bottom is helpful and the faucets should be at least 18 inches above its floor to permit the easy cleansing of pipettes, syringes, and other apparatus. Hot running water is desirable, and a water suction pump a must for the proper cleaning and drying of laboratory glassware.

Although only a small refrigerator is needed, it should be set on a platform to bring its contents waist high or higher. Space under the platform may be made a repository for infrequently used and cumbersome equipment.

The surface area of the counter should be at least 60 inches wide and 30 inches deep for each person working in the laboratory. (A group might well employ two technicians whose time would overlap. If their time is to be used efficiently they must be able to keep out of each other's way.)

Shelving over the work space and elsewhere in the laboratory should be built with its specific purpose in mind. Eight-inch clearance and 4-inch depth is quite sufficient to accommodate most reagent bottles and provides more shelving area in the same wall space. A deeper and more substantial shelf over the sink will support larger bottles for standard solutions used in quantity. A bookshelf should be close at hand.

Piped compressed air is a refinement but gas outlets will be desirable in the larger office laboratories.

Apart from the working space, a table will be necessary for venipuncture materials, the reclining arm for venipuncture, and the receptacle to receive blood or fomites, together with a chair for the patient. In the solo practitioner's office this may well have to be in the examining or even consulting room. In any case, provision should be made for the presence of a parent or companion for the patient's moral support. A chair should be available to him also against the eventuality of sympathetic syncope. Similarly a couch should be not too distant, for brief recovery from such contingencies.

PRIVACY

The collection of urine, stool, and vaginal secretions must be made easy and with a minimum of inconvenience and embarrassment to the patient and doctor alike. To this end office planning should permit ready communication between examining room,

TABLE 1 *

Laboratory Equipment

Instruments

Centrifuge (clinical)
Refrigerator
Microscope (preferably binocular)
with mechanical stage
Substage lamp with ground glass
and blue filter
Hemoglobinometer, Sahli cedar Immersion oil, Shillaber's
Balsam or plastic mounting material
Hemacytometer
Timing clock

Mechanical counter
(Photoelectric colorimeter standardized for several tests)
Urinometer (hydrometer type with bulb)
Chapman water suction with head for cleaning pipettes (blood and Wintrobe tubes)
Lens paper
Filter paper
Electrocardiograph

Glassware

Test tubes, brushes for same
Centrifuge tubes, brushes for same
Graduated cylinders
    100 ml.
    50 ml.
    25 ml.
    10 ml.
Funnels
    10 cm. size
Beakers (graduated in ml. and oz.)
    1000 ml.
    500 ml.
    100 ml.
    50 ml.
(Water cells and tubes for photelometer)
Medicine dropper pipettes
Hematology bottles

Chemistry bottles
Chemistry test tubes and stoppers
3 syringes, 5 cc.
2 syringes, 10 cc.
1 syringe, 30 cc.
5 hypodermic needles, No. 20
50-ml. burette with stand
Sahli tubes and pipettes
Microscope slides
Cover slips
Blood count pipettes (Bard-Parker)
Wintrobe tubes and pipettes
Alcohol lamp (and/or Bunsen burner)
Glass tubing
Diluting pipettes, 1 ml. to 10 ml.
Bell jar for microscope
Specimen bottles (blood and urine)

Miscellaneous

Textbooks
Facial tissues
Containers for mailing; state, commercial, etc.

Report forms
Covered refuse can
Card file
Scotch tape

* From the *Medical Clinics of North America* (September, 1953), p. 1529.

laboratory and lavatory without necessitating exposure to the view of anyone in the waiting room.

EQUIPMENT

Table 1 lists the essential materials that may form the basis of a small office laboratory. Together with the reagents listed in

TABLE 2 *
LABORATORY REAGENTS
Hematology

Wright's stain
Buffer phosphate solution (pH 6.4) 0.07
0.36 per cent HCl (0.1 N). Dilute 1 cc. commercial HCl to 100 cc.
Hayem's or Gower's solution (Gower's solution, 6.25 gm. Na_2SO_4 and 16.67 gm. glacial acetic acid in 100 cc. water)
Turck's solution
Brilliant cresyl blue

Urine

Benedict's solution (qualitative)	Acetest or acetone test (Denco)
Roberts' reagent	Nitrazine paper
Ammonia water	Sulkowitch reagent
Sodium nitroprusside crystals	1.45 per cent silver nitrate solution
Ammonium sulfate crystals	Potassium chromate, 20 per cent
Clinitest	Ferric chloride, 10 per cent

General

Anticoagulants (see text)	Alcohol, ethyl 95 per cent, 70 per cent antiseptic
Distilled water	
Acetone	Alconox or other detergent cleanser
Ether	H_2SO_4—K_2CrO_4 cleaning solution
Alcohol, methyl	Xylol

Miscellaneous

Gram's stain set
Commercial test kits
  Hematest
  Wilkerson-Heftmann screening blood sugar kit
  Ictotest
Potassium hydroxide, 10 per cent
Topfer's reagent
Phenolphthalein
Pandy's solution

* From the *Medical Clinics of North America* (September, 1953), p. 1530.

Table 2, they will suffice for performing those clinical tests most frequently indicated in the course of the general practice of office medicine. A few of these items deserve brief comment.

The centrifuge must be of good quality, whether of the angle type or free-swinging, with a sturdy protective jacket and capable of 2500 to 3000 r.p.m. Hematocrit determinations made on an inferior centrifuge will be unreliable.

Photoelectric colorimeters are expensive, of intricate design, and subject to easy deviation from standardization. While providing a high degree of accuracy when properly operated, they are subject to many technical errors in the hands of the untutored. The widespread custom of using photelometers on the basis of standardizations made by the manufacturer is universally decried by clinical pathologists and most medical technologists. Such instruments have no place in the solo practitioner's office, nor in any laboratory that does not employ a technician conversant with the mechanism and idiosyncrasies of these instruments.

The electrocardiograph is likewise a highly specialized instrument, and should be used only under the direction of a physician specifically trained in the inscription and interpretation of tracings. Technically, the instrument is subject to less caprice than the photelometer discussed above, and deviations from mechanical perfection of operation will be immediately obvious to the trained interpreter.

The basal metabolism instrument is not included in this list of laboratory impedimenta, since we feel that its legitimate uses are limited in general practice and the technic of performance is so refined that the infrequent occasion for basal metabolic rate determination would materially reduce its reliability. Similarly, the physical conditions requisite for the achievement of a truly basal state of the patient are difficult to provide in an office. The recording of the test in the home is likewise fraught with practical difficulties.

Specimen bottles and medicine droppers should have readily

identifying features, lest the wrong anticoagulant be used, or a dropper used in urinalysis find its way into a prescription bottle. Likewise, specimen bottles should be adapted to use in the home and the doctor's bag as well as in the office. This implies minimum size, sturdy construction, and tight, firm stoppers, preferably of the screw-on type. Community laboratories, whether commercial or governmental, usually provide their own containers for mailing. The office laboratory should be well stocked with these at all times.

It may seem superfluous to suggest that attention be given to assuring the availability of up-to-date textbooks till one reflects that the practicing physician starts his career with his medical school text, probably already seven or more years old and containing discarded, inferior, and even inaccurate procedural material.

The introduction of new equipment and new procedures will serve the incidental purposes of giving a fresh look to the laboratory and providing new interest for the technician.

Facial or toilet tissues and a covered refuse can are a courtesy certainly due and appreciated by the patient subjected to the intimate indignities contingent on a number of laboratory examinations. The unprompted provision of fresh perineal pads similarly displays thoughtfulness for the patient's comfort.

Laboratory Equipment for the Doctor's Bag

Many of the laboratory data necessary to private practice will be derived from patients confined to the home. Materials for the collection and transportation of specimens must be carried in the doctor's bag or car. Some highly significant tests can be performed at the bedside if a few simple reagents are included (notably those for glucose, acetone, blood in the urine, and for melena). Hemoglobin determination at the bedside is not feasible, the so-called Tallqvist method being totally unreliable.

Containers for many routine studies (urine, stool, sputum) can be gleaned from the household, the prerequisites being cleanliness and tight covering.

MAINTENANCE

The clinical laboratory must be constantly scrutinized for the repair or replacement of faulty equipment; cleaning, oiling, or readjustment of moving parts; replacement of chipped or scratched glassware; renewal of deteriorating reagents; and the depletion of expendable materials. While the supervision of this phase of laboratory function will rightfully be the responsibility of the technician, the clinician should likewise be alert to needs and freely and promptly provide, repair, or replace any and all equipment and material that will contribute to the laboratory's efficiency, usefulness, and pleasant atmosphere.

REPERTOIRE

It is inevitable that the more numerous and diversified the tests performed, the higher the overhead, and therefore the higher the cost to the patient of the individual test. However, a reasonably extensive repertoire will enhance the usefulness and prestige of the laboratory.

The number of different tests a laboratory may aspire to provide will depend entirely upon the need. This is not to say that a good laboratory cannot develop a market for itself. Indeed it can and it should. Where physicians have had to do without, they may be slow to make use of additional facilities till they are familiarized with the purpose and assistance of the service afforded. For example, the hematocrit is still used far less in community offices and hospitals than is merited by the simplicity and informativeness of the test. The same applies to many of the more recently introduced procedures.

To be reliable and economical, a test must be done frequently. Every test should be of sufficient clinical significance to justify its being done in a large per cent of cases that will yield normal values, even though this presupposes an additional financial burden on the aggregate patient clientele.

Obviously, the needs and services of a solo doctor's office laboratory will be significantly less extensive than those of the laboratory in the group clinic. It is, indeed, the greater demand of a group of doctors on the laboratory (and other ancillary services) that contributes to the increased efficiency and reliability of such services. This may properly be considered an advantage of group practice over solo practice.

Finally, the geographic location of the laboratory in relation to population and health centers will also dictate to some degree the scope of laboratory services. The office laboratory must be planned with the availability of laboratory services from other sources — i.e., commercial, hospital, municipal, and state laboratories — in mind if costly and needless reduplications are to be avoided.

Table 3 indicates a listing of the more common laboratory examinations one might expect for a solo practitioner's office in populous areas, and for the small group practice laboratory or for a country doctor's office remote from commercial, hospital, or state laboratories. The final column lists laboratory determinations offering real and reproducible clinical information in the hands of experts dealing frequently with the rarer clinical syndromes calling for such determinations. They are not for the offices of smaller groups and less specialized clinicians, being expensive, infrequently in demand, and technically difficult.

The office repertoire need not include blood typing and cross matching, for instance, since transfusion is rarely indicated outside a hospital. Neither is it practical to include tests for which reliable public facilities are available and urgency is of relatively little importance (serological test for syphilis, tubercle bacillus smears and cultures, and other tests).

TABLE 3 *

TESTS FOR THE OFFICE LABORATORY

	Solo Practitioner	Small Group, or Remote Laboratory of Country Practitioner	Probably Unjustifiable
Urine	Routine (appearance, pH, specific gravity, glucose, acetone, albumin, microscopic) Bile 24-hour quantitative sugar Bilirubin	Diacetic acid Phenolsulfonphthalein test Quantitative albumin Bence-Jones protein	Ketosteroids Hormones Pregnancy Urobilinogen
	Mosenthal concentration and dilution Chlorides; calcium, 24-hour qualitative		
Blood	Routine (hemoglobin, hematocrit, white blood count, differential) Erythrocyte sedimentation rate Blood sugar (screening) Bleeding and clotting Red blood count Mean corpuscular hemoglobin concentration	Chlorides and bicarbonates Reticulocytes Fungi Glucose tolerance test Blood parasites Prothrombin time	Electrolyte partition gases Serum proteins Vitamins Flame photometry Liver function tests Spectrophotometry Microanalysis L. E. test Protein bound iodine and I^{131} Thorn's eosinophil count
	Photoelectric cell use Fragility and sickling Typing and cross matching Serologic test for syphilis Nonprotein nitrogen Color index Mean corpuscular volume Mean corpuscular hemoglobin		
Stool	Appearance Blood and pus Pinworms		Fats, chemical analyses and others
		Ova and parasites	
Stomach		Gastric analysis Duodenal drainage	Concentration of acid-fast bacilli or malignant cells
Spinal fluid	Appearance, cells, protein	Glucose Wright or Gram stain	Serology, colloidal gold, quantitative protein, culture
Sputum	Appearance, quantity, blood	Methylene blue, Gram, acid-fast and Wright stains	Concentration of acid-fast bacilli Fungi
Bacteriology	See text	Cultures for B. coli and β-hemolytic streptococci Blood agar plates and media for growth and transportation Gram, Loeffler's and acid-fast stains	Culture, identification and determinations of sensitivity to various antibiotics
Miscellaneous	Venous pressure, vital capacity circulation time	Electrocardiogram Bromsulphalein Icteric index, etc.	Basal metabolism rate X-ray Papanicolaou interpretation
	Fluoroscopy Papanicolaou collection and fixation		

* From the *Medical Clinics of North America* (September, 1953), p. 1527.

Bacteriology, like photoelectric colorimetry, is a highly technical exercise and should not be undertaken in most small laboratories.

Liver function tests are legion. A few such tests are relatively simple of performance. However, the multiple functions of the liver, and its interrelations with other metabolic systems and with the endocrines, make evaluation of its performance a vastly complex and still imperfectly understood procedure. For this reason the simpler liver function tests are of limited value standing alone. It is only with the information derived from a battery of tests, most of which are too complex for our purposes, that a differential diagnosis can be made in the most obscure hepatic disorders.

Recent Contributions to Office Laboratory Repertoire

A recently developed urine bilirubin test has proved an additional aid in the bedside supervision of subclinical hepatitis, as in healing infectious hepatitis. This test provides one more measure of liver function upon which the duration of bed rest may depend. Inexpensive, it is also more specific than either a shake test for bile in the urine or determination of the serum icteric index.

There is accumulating evidence that the excretion of calcium in the urine, as measured in an aliquot of 24-hour specimen by use of Sulkowitch's qualitative test reagent, is a practical and reliable measure of the osteolytic progression of bone metastases from advanced mammary cancer. Since therapy is symptomatic, depending on the arrest or progression of the disease as determined clinically, this affords practical information in the office and bedside management of this disease.

Promise is shown in the field of bedside (or office) determination of blood and plasma electrolytes, notably chloride, bicarbonate, and most recently potassium. A facile method of blood nonprotein nitrogen measurement has not yet been perfected. At present these procedures are for the better and more ambitious group laboratories to explore.

TECHNICS

Technics, like equipment, get rusty from disuse and deteriorate without refurbishing and periodic overhauling. As with stock reagents, stock procedures need freshening and replacement. The essence of good technic, then, is a constant awareness of the fallibility of routinization, and the unceasing objective inquiry into the purpose, procedure, and pitfalls of each performance of every examination. The doctor will do well to scrutinize the laboratory data critically and to question any discrepancy between it and clinical findings, not for the purpose of placing blame, but only to correct errors wherever found.

The validity of the individual test may be tried against other laboratories with duplicate samples of the same blood, or by submitting both such duplicates under different names to the laboratory without the technician's knowledge. This is an accepted method of checking technics and should be discussed in principle with the technician.

There are several features of office laboratory procedure that differ materially from procedure in hospitals.

In the office laboratory the convenient time of collecting specimens is during or shortly before the patient's visit to the attending physician. Hence, the blood may show a postprandial leucocytosis, lipemia, or elevation of sugar concentration. An "early morning specimen" of urine may be 8 hours old on delivery, and unsuitable for microscopic study.

Specimens taken during house calls may be several hours old, shaken up, or exposed to excesses of heat or cold, unless attention is paid to these details.

Every laboratory must be alert to the importance of meticulous cleanliness, quantitative precision, appropriate sterilization and drying of needles, syringes, and containers. Time spent by the physician in the instruction of self or technician in the niceties of venipuncture technic, the sharpening and cleansing of needles, and the preparation and aftercare of the patient's punctured vein will make the experience a decreasingly traumatic one for all concerned.

COMMUNITY FACILITIES

As already intimated, the office laboratory will prove must useful as a complementary adjunct to existing laboratory services available to any physician establishing a practice in a new community. To endeavor to supplant or compete with reliable and prompt laboratory services already adequately providing a community need is not only extravagant, but a disservice to all concerned — laboratories, patients, and physicians. The community hospital laboratory in particular needs the support of outpatient referrals from the members of the staff. This support should be given gladly wherever feasible, for the hospital is the focal point of the physician's practice.

The physician's own clinical pathological excursions then will depend to no little extent on the availability, reliability, and scope of community laboratories, be they in the local hospital, commercial, municipal, or state and national laboratories. Availability, of course, implies the relative factors of distance, public conveyance, frequency of use of a specific procedure, speed or urgency of completion (from the decision to require it to receipt of the report), and stability of the material.

While it is quite within the province of the laboratory personnel to be familiar with and responsible for all this data, the physician himself will wisely visit not only the community hospital's clinical laboratory, but also any commercial laboratory he is going to patronize. For while some commercial laboratories perform to meet excellent standards, most of these need close scrutiny, particularly in the matter of uncritical acceptance of specimens without regard to conditions of delivery. Many commercial laboratories fall below the minimum standards of technic and reliability, a fact readily recognized from a visit.

There are, unfortunately, laboratories whose work is not only inaccurate, but also irresponsible. These are best shunned entirely.

While one may well assume the validity of most municipal and state clinical laboratories, it is well to appraise the work done and the appropriateness of the reports received. A visit may establish a rapport and mutual respect that a decade of correspondence might not achieve.

The United States Public Health Service publishes a yearly *Directory of State and Territory Health Authorities* (4) for those interested in a national view in anticipation of selecting a region for settlement. State authorities will provide detailed information of district, county, and municipal facilities.

While much of the foregoing seems obvious enough, it is a deplorable fact that many community hospital laboratories and a large proportion of practicing physicians are either unfamiliar with the public services available to them or ignore them for any of a number of reasons. The establishment of a familiar liaison with such facilities early in one's practice, while time hangs heavy, will lead to a habit pattern useful throughout one's professional lifetime.

PERSONNEL

"If you want it done well, do it yourself." Unfortunately the successful practitioner will soon find that his clinical responsibilities do not leave him the time needed for the corresponding laboratory studies. With the introduction of either a factotum secretary-receptionist-bookkeeper-laboratory technician, or of several ancillary personnel, his problems will be compounded. In either case there exists a personnel problem.

Implicit in much that has gone before has been a concern for personnel morale. This aspect of laboratory operation, in fact, represents the major complication of an office laboratory. In a facility where only the simpler tests are performed, a close clinical liaison affords the best stimulus to the technician's continued interest and to her appreciation of the significance and importance of her work. Repeated reminders of the contribution to diagnosis and treatment made by laboratory information, and discussion of the pathological physiology causing abnormal laboratory findings, will demonstrate appreciation too often unexpressed. Prompt, frank, and objective re-evaluation of tests affording discrepancies either incongruous or recurring with unlikely frequency will serve to convince the technician that laboratory reports are more than "window dressing" or sources of office income.

It is inconsistent to expect order and cleanliness of the laboratory and consequent meticulousness and accuracy of performance if adequate attention and funds are not contributed by the physician to the equipment and furnishings of the laboratory.

It is therefore incumbent upon the physician (a) to be fully cognizant of the technics, the sources of correctible error, the reproducibility, and the normal range and significant deviations of all tests performed in his office laboratory; (b) to assure the continued use, objective re-evaluation of accuracy, and reassessment of the current or alternative technics of performance; (c) to be familiar with the innovation of new technics or new tests appropriate for his laboratory as they appear in the literature, and to discuss, practice, and carefully appraise new procedures with the technician, checking by multiple samples and comparison with the findings of other experienced laboratories; (d) to make available the current literature in the current textbooks of clinical pathology, in the *American Journal of Medical Technology,* and perhaps the *American Journal of Clinical Pathology,* or even in the *Journal of Laboratory and Clinical Medicine* and the *Journal of Clinical Investigation.* The first of these journals should be considered basic to an office laboratory. The others can be scanned briefly in a medical library at intervals, and procedures and discussions suitable for office use appropriated.

The personnel problem in a group clinic affords one more hazard, that of the relations between the laboratory and the clinicians. This is specifically a matter of clearly defining authority and responsibility. Since the clinicians will have much to do with the preparing of the patient and the collection and transportation of samples, they must be kept constantly aware of the importance of discharging this responsibility. Similarly, the laboratory must be represented by one familiar with clinical implications.

A group clinic laboratory then should be under the direct administrative and professional supervision of a physician who in turn is responsible to the staff for the maintenance of high standards of performance.

PATIENT ACCEPTANCE

The introduction of laboratory studies into the family doctor's role even now meets with patient resistance in a large percentage of the population. This is a reflection more on medical socioeconomics than on medical education. If the physician sends his patients to a commercial or hospital laboratory for studies the patient will resent the added expense more than he will doubt the doctor's clinical acumen, but if the diagnostic studies are done in the doctor's office and therefore the fee to the office is increased, the doctor will promptly be suspect for "overcharging." Yet, in this day of wider knowledge and definitive therapy, it is inexcusable to attend any but the briefest and most trivial of ills without benefit of the supportive information of basic laboratory studies. That symptomatic therapy continues to be the rule rather than the exception is attributable in part to economic pressures and in part to professional lethargy. For an explanation to the patient is time-consuming and not always satisfactory. In many communities the performance of laboratory studies will be an innovation and patients are sometimes even slower than doctors to accept change.

Nevertheless, experience has shown that this service is ultimately not only accepted, but appreciated and even boasted of by patients at first skeptical and resistant.

FINANCING AND ADMINISTRATION

A laboratory should not be a source of significant profit. It should pay its way, including a fair price for the physician's time, effort, and experience in supervision and administration. The more versatile the service is, the more costly the operation, and the higher the rates to the patient. Any scale of prices will have to be adjusted accordingly, and individual charges will necessarily be tailored to the patient's resources and his total medical expenses. In any case, the laboratory fees should be clearly distinguished in the patient's mind from professional fees and the cost indicated in a general way before the tests are done.

Much of the administrative responsibility has already been outlined. Here it is necessary only to re-emphasize the importance of a clear understanding of the respective spheres of responsibility of technician and physician, and, in medical groups, of the clinician in charge and the rest of the medical staff.

It is well to emphasize here the obvious but oft neglected obligation to record all data, both on the patient's record and in the laboratory file.

SUMMARY

The addition of basic laboratory services to the professional services of a doctor, while conducive to significantly superior medical practice, will introduce a number of ponderable obstacles and responsibilities. Some of these have been discussed briefly. Space and equipment requirements are outlined.

It is emphasized that laboratory data are indispensable to the practice of modern medicine with its clearer understanding of physiology and pathology and its wealth of definitive therapy. It is recommended that the office laboratory, whether for solo practitioner or medical group, restrict its operations to a minimum, serving only to complement the services of the larger established clinical laboratories of hospitals, community and state. To facilitate the full utilization of these is, however, a function of the office laboratory.

The essential factor of a vital and effective laboratory is a close liaison between technician and physician, with reciprocal discussion and criticism of procedure, technic, sources of error, and innovations.

Since personnel morale is the major stumbling block to competent office laboratory services, attention is drawn to the fine line between sufficient repetition to assure sustained perfection of technic and a wide enough repertoire to hold the technician's interest. The problem of patient acceptance is evaluated, and the responsibility of the physician to educate his patients to a better type of medical care is shown to be justly rewarded.

REFERENCES

1. HAM, T. H. *A Syllabus of Laboratory Examinations in Clinical Diagnosis.* Longwood Publishing Co., 1950.
2. BOARDMAN, D. W. The Doctor's Office Laboratory. *The Medical Clinics of North America,* September, 1953.
3. TODD, J. C., SANFORD, A. H., and WELLS, B. B. *Clinical Diagnosis by Laboratory Methods.* (12th ed.) Philadelphia: Saunders, 1953.
4. *Directory of State and Territorial Health Authorities.* Public Health Service Publication No. 75, Department of Health, Education and Welfare. Washington, D. C.: United States Government Printing Office.

13

Drugs and Medical Supplies

by Arthur C. DeGraff

THE PHYSICIAN, like any trained craftsman, requires the tools and equipment necessary to the practice of his profession. What he will need will vary considerably, depending on the type of practice and location. The general practitioner whose office is not within a short distance of a well-equipped hospital or medical center will require the greatest diversity of supplies so that he can properly handle all emergency situations. The doctor who is a member of a medical group will probably need to make the smallest outlay, since presumably he will have access to all the facilities of the group or center. However, he will need certain basic supplies for his personal use. The psychiatrist needs the least equipment, but even he would probably want to examine his patient, particularly if he combines neurology with psychiatry. Therefore a certain minimum amount of equipment will be required in his office. It is important to know whether or not a pharmacy is near or available at all times. For instance, in country districts it may be necessary for a physician to keep on hand many drugs for emergency use, whereas in the city a physician could easily obtain such drugs from a pharmacy within a few minutes. In some suburban areas pharmacies are closed at night, so a physician may find it desirable to have on hand a few emergency remedies if he should be called out to see a patient during those hours.

The doctor's office is his base for supplies. If he makes a house call, he should ascertain as closely as possible what he may need for any particular situation. Although a doctor's bag can and should contain materials and drugs for emergency treatment, all contingencies cannot be anticipated. Some physicians fit up the luggage compartment of the car with equipment needed for emergency work. This is particularly important when the physician is practicing in an industrial or farming area where accidents may occur and emergency surgical treatment may be required. Even so, there are times when a doctor will find it necessary to take along something additional from his office for a particular case.

Elsewhere in this book the general layout of the doctor's office is considered. The special equipment, however, that should be available to practice medicine may properly be taken up in this chapter. It is not necessary to spend a great deal of money on expensive equipment. On the other hand, the physician must be sure that what he buys is adequate for his needs and rugged enough to stand the daily routine. This is particularly true of the examining table, a comfortable, adjustable one being essential. The mistake is often made of getting too narrow a table. It should not be less than 24 inches wide and should be long enough when fully extended to allow a patient 6 feet tall to recline on it comfortably. If practice is confined entirely to internal medicine, a simple massage table with a sponge rubber top and an arrangement so that the head end can be raised to different levels may be sufficient. On the other hand, if gynecological or proctoscopic examinations are to be made, a much more elaborate type of table is needed. The various manufacturers of examining tables usually exhibit their products at medical conventions; a particularly complete display is usually to be seen at the annual convention of the American Medical Association. There should be accurate scales with a rod to measure height. Special scales may be needed for infants if the physician practices pediatrics. A cabinet with shelves and drawers to contain minor equipment is also needed. A mercury manometer attached to the wall is quite convenient and always accessible.

Other equipment should include a small sterilizer, thermometers (both oral and rectal), syringes and needles, bandages, adhesive tape, tongue depressors, flashlight, ophthalmoscope with otoscope attachment, urine glasses, and a small bedpan (to collect specimens of urine from female patients). If minor surgery or follow-up surgical treatment of patients operated on in the hospital is to be done in the office, the necessary instruments and materials for dressings should be available.

A towel service is usually available in urban areas to take care of towels, sheets, examining gowns, and other linen. In the absence of such service, paper towels and gowns, which can be thrown away after each examination, are quite satisfactory and are procurable in many different types and grades.

The stock of medicines in a doctor's office should be kept at a minimum. Wherever possible medicine should be prescribed, not dispensed. This leaves the patient free to obtain his medicine from any pharmacy and avoids giving him the impression that the doctor is making a profit on the medicine or is having him return for that alone. The patient should come to the physician for a medical opinion, not for renewal of medicine, and the doctor should never send a patient to a particular pharmacist except when the patient asks him to recommend a pharmacist near by. In that case it may be well to give the names of two or three places where the prescription may be filled. The doctor should have his prescription pads printed himself, in preference to using those that bear advertising of a pharmacy or a pharmaceutical house. Because of the fact that many drugs are prescribed in tablet form already made by the manufacturer, the pharmacist does not have the job of compounding prescriptions that he had many years ago. There are still some fields, however, notably in dermatology, where the skill and training of the pharmacist is important in making up a proper prescription for an ointment or lotion. The pharmacist can be of great help to the physician in suggesting the best vehicle to use for such medications. The pharmacist can also be of help in making up special forms of medication that are not available in package form from the manufacturer, such as suppositories of digitalis.

A few drugs in easily injectable form should be available in the office at all times. These should include morphine, a mercurial diuretic, penicillin, epinephrine, atropine, nalorphine (Nalline) hydrochloride, meperidine (Demerol) hydrochloride, aminophylline, ouabain, and procaine amide. Other standard drugs include nitroglycerin, tincture of iodine, spirits of ammonia, aspirin, meperidine (Demerol) hydrochloride tablets, ephedrine, and antacid tablets (such as magnesium trisilicate and aluminum hydroxide).

A physician who must make emergency calls will need to carry a certain amount of equipment and drugs in his bag. There will, of course, be considerable individual variation. The following should be carried:

Equipment

Blood pressure apparatus
Finger cots
Ophthalmoscope and otoscope
Prescription blanks
Reflex hammer
Small flashlight
Sterile needles (sizes used for hypodermic intramuscular and intravenous use may be carried soaked in alcohol in special metal case)
Sterile swabs
Stethoscope
1.0 cc. syringe (sterilized)
2.0 cc. syringe (sterilized)
Tape measure
Tongue depressors
Tuning fork
Urine specimen bottle

Drugs

Sterile distilled water in rubber-stopped vial or in ampules
Small bottle of alcohol

Penicillin
Morphine sulfate
Atropine sulfate
Meperidine
  (Demerol) hydro-
  chloride
Epinephrine hydro-
  chloride (1–1000)

Syringe, ampule solution, and needle may be obtained in sterile unit
ready for immediate use

Nalorphine (Nalline) hydrochloride (narcotic antagonist),
  2 cc. ampules (10 mg.)
Procaine amide (Pronestyl) hydrochloride, vial 10 cc. (100 mg. per cc.)
Picrotoxin (for use in barbiturate poisoning), 2 ampules
  (ampule 1 cc. contains 3 mg.)
Pentobarbital (Nembutal) sodium, 2 ampules sterile
  solution 5 cc. containing 0.24 gm.
Insulin

Additional Drugs That Might Be Useful

Aminophylline 10 cc. ampules (0.25 gm.) for intravenous use
Amobarbital (Amytal) sodium, ampule 0.065 gm.
Apomorphine hydrochloride hypodermic, tablet 5 mg.
Calcium gluconate, 10 cc. of 10 per cent solution
Ergotamine tartrate (Gynergen), ampule 0.5 cc. (0.25 mg.)
Glucose, 50 per cent, ampule 50 cc.
Magnesium sulfate, 50 per cent solution, ampule 2 cc.
Mercaptomerin (Thiomerin), vial 10 cc.
Neostigmine (Prostigmine) methyl sulfate, 1:2000 and 1:4000 solutions
Nicotinic acid, 100 mg. in 10 cc.
Nitroglycerin tablet, 0.3 or 0.6 mg.
Ouabain ampules 0.1 mg. and 0.5 mg.
Pentobarbital (Nembutal) capsules, 0.1 gm.
Phenobarbital tablets, 30 mg.
Tetracaine (Pontocaine), 1 per cent, for ophthalmic use
Silver nitrate (sticks)
Sodium amytal, ampule 0.065 gm.
Syrup of ipecac

Surgical and Laboratory Materials

Adhesive tape, ½-inch and 4-inch sizes
Bandage scissors
Bandages, 1-, 2-, and 3-inch sizes
Band-aids
Benzalkonium (Zephiran) chloride, 1:1000 aqueous solution
Blood count set

Ethyl chloride spray
Gauze, ½-inch, for nasal packing
Gloves, 1 pair
Laboratory test tubes, oxalated and plain, for blood samples
Levine tube
Lubricating jelly
Myringotomy knife
Sterile gauze pads
Small surgical kit including needle holder, thumb clamp, small hemostats,
    and scalpel; also sterile sutures and eyeless needles, various sizes
Tourniquets (3)

Because of the recent federal law regulating the refilling of prescriptions, it is important for a doctor to indicate to the patient on the prescription how many times it may be renewed. It should be pointed out that such drugs as narcotics and sedatives require a new prescription because of federal and state laws. The prescription blank should be modeled after the following:

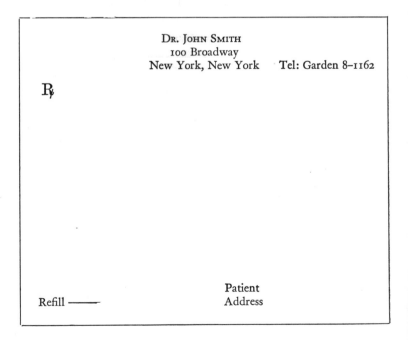

DR. JOHN SMITH
100 Broadway
New York, New York   Tel: Garden 8–1162

℞

Refill ———

Patient
Address

It is very important that a physician be on guard against giving narcotic prescriptions to addicts. Government and state agents check narcotic prescriptions with the pharmacist from time to time and if it is noted that a particular patient is getting narcotic prescriptions filled regularly, the doctor is called upon to explain. Moreover, the federal government demands that physicians report all drug addicts. If a physician has under his care a patient who has intractable pain, such as may be the case with inoperable carcinoma, he should get in touch with the narcotic bureau in his area and explain the circumstances. The use of morphine and other opium derivatives comes under the provisions of the Harrison Narcotic Act. Synthetic analogues of morphine, methadone and meperidine are subject to the same regulations as morphine itself.

The barbiturates are habit-forming, and if given in large enough doses over a period of time, withdrawal symptoms on stopping them can be severe. The greatest danger with the barbiturates is that patients may take an excess for suicidal purposes.

One of the doctor's biggest problems is keeping up with the advances in drug therapy. The gap between a new discovery and its application in medicine has been narrowed markedly over the past few years. Many factors are responsible for this, but perhaps the greatest is the tremendous lay interest in medicine, as indicated by articles in lay magazines and newspapers. The large newspaper chains and press services cover every medical and scientific meeting, in search of new and sensational medical discoveries, and there is still an unfortunate temptation to publish sensational and not always accurate reports. The doctor is then besieged by his patients, who want such treatment for themselves. It is unfortunate that frequently even important new drugs are reported to the press before they have been described in medical journals. Such premature publicity may be dangerous because a drug may not have been used long enough to determine its side actions and toxic effects. The physician should not allow himself to be persuaded to use any new drug until it has been studied carefully and released for general distribution, with appropriate safeguards, by the Food and Drug Administration.

New drugs are generally developed in the laboratories of the pharmaceutical houses or the research laboratories of medical schools. If they are found to have therapeutic value greater than drugs already generally available, and have little or no toxic effects in the dosage recommended, the Food and Drug Administration may allow their release for general use, upon application by the pharmaceutical house distributing them. The drug company then through advertising in medical journals and by mail acquaints the doctor with the essential medical facts about the new drug, particularly the indications, methods of administration, dosage, and side actions.

The larger drug companies maintain a staff of detail men who visit the doctor at his office prepared to answer questions regarding their new products and to supply him with samples and medical literature. Although an occasional detail man may try to apply salesmanship pressure, they are, in the main, highly trained and concerned with helping the physician to get the information that he needs.

The doctor must remember, however, in dealing with information that is handed out to him by drug companies, that they are primarily interested in acquainting him with their own products. Therefore, other sources of information should be available. Attendance at medical meetings where original papers are read by investigators of the drugs will, of course, give the doctor first-hand information. Reference to current medical journals, especially the *Journal of the American Medical Association,* will be of the greatest help, especially to the general practitioner. The recommendations of the Council on Pharmacy and Chemistry are also published from time to time in the *Journal.*

Other sources of information are also desirable, particularly since the same drug may be marketed under many different names. For instance, digitoxin is available under such trade names as Crystodigin, Purodigin, and Digitaline Nativelle. A volume known as the *Modern Drug Encyclopedia and Therapeutic Index,* now in its fifth edition, contains all this information. It is particularly helpful when a doctor hears from a patient the name of a drug completely unknown to him. In looking it up in this book, he usually finds it is a mixture of common drugs with a fancy name coined by the manufacturer. Although this book must be purchased, supplements are distributed free to all physicians every two or three months under the title *Modern Drugs.* Another source of information is the *Physician's Desk Reference.* This book is distributed free to all physicians. Since it is financed by the drug companies whose products are listed in the book, products of other drug companies may not be listed. No supplements of this book are issued.

Once a year the Council on Pharmacy and Chemistry of the American Medical Association issues a book entitled *New and Nonofficial Remedies.* This book lists and describes all drugs that have received the approval of the council. Every five years there is a new revision of the United States *Pharmacopoeia,* which lists and sets standards for all drugs considered of importance therapeutically by a group of experts on its revision committee. Interim supplements are published when necessary during the five-year period between revisions of the entire volume. Any drug that is listed in the U.S.P. must conform to its standards and is subject to seizure by agents of the Food and Drug Administration of the United States Government if substandard and transported from one state to another. Manufacturers of substandard drugs are subject to prosecution. There is also available an *Epitome of the Pharmacopoeia and National Formulary,* which is a small volume listing all the useful preparations and their doses that are found in the larger parent volume.

One must be sure to secure drugs from reputable, well-established manufacturers, who have technical superiority and are most careful in maintaining the quality of their products. There are fly-by-night concerns that sell substandard drugs and then go out of business before the government agents can catch up with them. Unusual bargains advertised by mail should in particular be carefully scrutinized before buying.

An annual review of drug therapy that is well worth owning has been published each year since 1950 under the capable editorship of Dr. Harry Beckman, director of the Department of Pharmacology, Marquette University School of Medicine. This is entitled *Year Book of Drug Therapy* and is published by Year Book Publishers, Chicago. All the important articles on drug therapy published during the preceding year are reviewed in a concise and informative manner and editorial comment is frequent and to the point.

The physician never completes his education. Medical science is constantly advancing, so that he must make every effort to maintain his acquaintance with the new forms of diagnosis and therapy. He can do this only by keeping up with his medical literature and by contact with other physicians in his field at medical meetings or conferences where discussions are held. Refresher courses are available in medical colleges and centers and are also arranged by various national organizations, such as the American College of Physicians and the American Academy of General Practice. The medical staff conference at the local hospital is also important, in that it stimulates the physician to consult references on the case that is being presented.

14

The Office and Related Business Aspects *

by John A. Pond

ACCORDING TO a recent estimate issued in a public statement by the president of the Association of American Medical Colleges, the average student has devoted a minimum of nine to ten years of study and work after high school graduation to prepare himself for a career in medicine. The estimated average cost to him is given as $19,000 for this period, in addition to which the medical school has contributed another $10,000.

The business and financial problems facing the practitioner of medicine at the beginning of his career are therefore more difficult than in any other profession. In many cases he is already in debt of some sort even before he begins his practice. The demands and rigors of his educational and training period have often enough caused him to postpone marriage until he has qualified himself for practice, so that the additional burden of establishing a home and family life complicate further the over-all business and financial problem. It therefore behooves him to husband his resources in such a manner that his necessary investment and operating expenses are kept at a minimum until his increased income allows him to relax such efforts.

Certain basic considerations must guide him in establishing his

* Some of the material for this presentation was obtained through the courtesy of The American Surgical Trade Association. Acknowledgment with thanks is due Mr. Michael M. Artese for his help in screening the list of requirements.

office. These concern the basic equipment he has to buy; its cost; the further equipment he may need to purchase as his practice and income increase; the most reliable and economical sources of supply; the most practical methods of payment to suit his financial circumstances; transportation; and the location of his office.

The lists that follow are planned to include the initial equipment necessary for the dignified reception of patients and their adequate diagnosis and treatment. It is, of course, possible to get along with much less, and some doctors might even consider the lists inadequate. They are offered as a framework for consideration only, and the prices as typical for today and far from exact for every circumstance.

RECEPTION ROOM

The primary requirement for the reception room is a comfortable and relaxing atmosphere, undisturbed by the circulation of patients and personnel, yet close to the main entrance and receptionist's desk. Concerning size and seating capacity, no rules can be established, since the type and extent of expected practice and the system of appointments vary considerably with each physician. Some provision should be made in or near each reception room for hanging coats, hats, and umbrellas, and there should be a wall mirror near the entrance. Suggested equipment is:

1 Nurse's or receptionist's desk	$ 60.00
1 Posture chair	30.00
1 Settee (for 3 persons)	75.00
3 Occasional chairs ($20.00 each)	60.00
1 Center table	20.00
1 Smoking stand	12.00
1 Wardrobe cabinet	50.00
1 Wall mirror	25.00
Total	$332.00

CONSULTATION ROOM

With the possible exception of the dermatologist and the ophthalmologist, who usually combine the functions of consultation and examination in one room, every physician needs a separate private office. Although this room does not need to be very large in most cases, it should be attractively decorated and furnished, and it must afford complete privacy for conversations with patients and other callers. Generally, the preferred location for the consultation room is near the waiting room and close to the nurse's or receptionist's desk for the convenience of patients, who often complete their visits in this area alone. Suggested equipment is as follows:

1 Executive or kneehole-type desk	$100.00
1 Swivel-type armchair	50.00
3 Straight-back side chairs ($25.00 each)	75.00
1 Bookcase	60.00
1 Costumer	15.00
1 Wastebasket	2.00
1 Desk lamp	10.00
1 Card file	10.00
1 Weighing scale with measuring rod	60.00
1 Stand 16 by 20 inches for medications	20.00
1 Drinking cup dispenser with cups	3.00
Total	$405.00

EXAMINATION AND TREATMENT ROOMS

The number, size, layout, and equipment of rooms under this heading is determined by the volume of patients and by the type of service rendered. As a general rule, two rooms, preferably designed for interchangeable use, are recommended. Although it is perfectly feasible to practice in a suite containing only one room for the examination of patients, the additional expense in rent and equipment for a second room should be considered whenever the physician's practice or finances warrant. Suggested equipment and supplies are listed in the sections following.

Equipment

1 Examining and treatment table	$350.00
1 Instrument cabinet	200.00
1 Treatment cabinet	125.00
1 Instrument sterilizer, 16-inch size	100.00
1 Revolving stool	35.00
1 Waste receptacle	20.00
1 All chrome pedestal-type floor lamp	15.00
1 Set glass dressing jars	10.00
Equipment total	$855.00

Instruments and Sundries

Suggested items are:

1 Rectal speculum	$ 5.50
1 Set 3 vaginal specula	15.00
1 Pelvimeter	3.25
1 Electric headlight	6.25
1 Head mirror and headband	3.70
1 Ear and nasal dressing forceps	1.25
2 Straight hemostats ($2.95 each)	5.90
1 Needle holder	3.95
1 Suture scissors	2.15
1 Dissecting scissors	1.75
1 Bandage scissors	2.15
1 Dozen suture needles	1.50
1 Menda alcohol dispenser	1.75
1 Asepto catheter syringe, 1 oz.	.78
1 Dozen assorted Luer hypodermic needles	1.90
2 Luer syringes, 2 cc.	4.38
1 Luer syringe, 5 cc.	2.06
1 Luer syringe, 10 cc.	1.78

1	Luer syringe, 20 cc.	3.08
3	Nelaton S.R. catheters ($.42 each)	1.26
1	Thumb forceps	1.08
1	Tissue forceps	1.40
1	Clip forceps	4.25
1	Package of 100 suture clips	.40
1	Splinter forceps	1.25
1	Forceps jar	2.75
1	B.P. instrument tray	10.00
1	Quart B.P. germicide	1.75
1	Utility forceps	1.80
1	Nail drill	4.00
1	Splinter forceps, long	1.40
1	Cataract needle and spud	3.00
1	Nasal atomizer and bulb	3.40
1	Box tongue blades	1.20
1	Box applicators	.42
1	Roll cotton	.90
1	Roll adhesive	4.00
1	Adhesive rack	4.80
1	Gauze 12 inches x 5 yards	.90
1	Dozen bandages	2.10
3	Pairs rubber surgical gloves	1.35
1	Tourniquet	.70
1	Tube lubricating jelly	.49
1	Uterine dressing forceps	5.45
1	Desk thermometer set	2.50
1	Tube ethyl chloride	1.00
1	Instrument tray with cover, stainless steel	4.90
1	Ear and ulcer syringe	.50
1	Box 3 by 3-inch sterile pads	1.75
1	Drinking cup dispenser with cups	3.00
2	Office gowns	6.00
	Instruments and sundries total	$147.78

Additional Items

The following are desirable items that may be purchased as the practice grows:

Physiotherapy

1 Short-wave therapy machine	$750.00
1 Physiotherapy table	75.00
1 Internal timer	12.50
Total	$837.50

Basal Metabalor

1 Metabalor	$385.00
1 Wood table	60.00
1 Straight-back chair	15.00
Total	$460.00

SUMMARY OF INITIAL COSTS

From the preceding lists of suggested basic initial requirements, it would appear that the following summary of initial costs is reasonable in establishing an office to serve patients in general practice:

Reception room	$ 332.00
Consultation room	405.00
Examination and treatment room	
Equipment	855.00
Supplies	147.76
Total of initial basic requirements	$1739.76
Physiotherapy (optional)	837.50
Basal Metabalor (optional)	462.50
Total	$3039.76

Laboratory equipment, costing $500 to $600, and the doctor's bag and its contents, at around $150, must be added to the rough estimates given above. They are considered in other chapters.

NEEDS OF THE SPECIALIST

The suggestions made in the preceding lists are based on the needs of a general practitioner. The specialist would of course require modifications to include items suited to his particular specialty. The physician intending to specialize should explore the feasibility of locating his office in a medical arts building or a general clinical building of some sort, to enable him to have access to referable work from other physicians and to have the co-operative use of expensive diagnostic and clinical equipment. No attempt is made in this presentation to predict the needs of the specialist, as circumstances vary so greatly in every given situation.

PURCHASING

Using the suggested lists as guides to requirements and a tentative budget, the next problem is to determine where and how to buy the equipment and supplies. The first basic premise that the young physician should be willing to accept at the outset is that there is no suitable substitute for competition between suppliers to arrive at the lowest price available. Some inexperienced physicians may believe that it is below the dignity of their position in the community to buy competitively. There is no real basis in fact to feel this way. Most business concerns expect and welcome legitimate competition. The most important thing is to be fair to all and describe your needs exactly enough so that there is no question about the identity of your intended purchases. A little time spent in mailing a definitive list to a reasonable number of ethical and legitimate suppliers will pay substantial financial dividends. This procedure also establishes you as a continual potential customer, and suppliers will retain their interest in your needs and will continue to be interested in competing for your business.

Methods

The following methods of determining how to make your purchases should be investigated:

Talk with the purchasing agent, business manager, or administrator of some hospital with which you are acquainted, preferably a teaching hospital. Hospital personnel are usually anxious and willing to help a young physician get off to a good start. Inquire about the relative merits of various manufacturers' items and obtain information on manufacturers' catalogues of instruments, supplies, and equipment, to help you properly identify any item in regard to quality, grade and price.

Talk with the chief of staff in the teaching hospital where you obtained your training and get the benefit of his experience.

Ask the superintendent of nurses in any hospital about her experience with various kinds of merchandise and avoid buying items that do not stand hard use.

Mention your problems to the detail men who visit you. They probably see first-hand more doctors and nurses in private practice than any other single group of business representatives serving the medical profession, and can suggest where used equipment may be available.

Talk with the representatives of surgical supply houses who have been in the business a long time and can give the benefit of other doctors' mistakes under similar circumstances.

Consult telephone books of the major communities in your area or beyond for business houses listed in the classified section as serving your profession.

From the classified telephone directories also make a list of suppliers whose business it is to buy and sell used medical and surgical equipment. There are many long-established businesses of integrity and reliability who deal in used equipment, and excellent bargains can be found in this way. Great care should be taken, however, in buying used equipment of a mechanical or electrical nature.

The procedures mentioned may seem to be a lot of bother as well as time-consuming, but a saving of 10 per cent on an expenditure that may amount to $2000 is equal to $200, and in the initial stages of a new practice this is a useful amount to have available for some other purpose.

Cash or Credit

A part of the buying consideration is the amount of ready capital available for cash purchasing. Ready cash puts one in a better bargaining position to obtain lower prices as well as cash discounts. A loan from the bank should be considered preferable to paying higher prices for merchandise for extended credit. The cash buyer is also free to deal with anyone without embarrassment. The credit buyer, especially in the medical profession, sometimes feels obliged to lean on one supplier, who in turn is entitled to more money for his goods and services if he must wait over an extended period for payment. If it is decided that credit buying suits one's purposes best, most large and established surgical supply firms will sell supplies on the basis of 33⅓ per cent down with the balance in six equal monthly payments. Carrying charges and interest are not added, but list prices are usually charged when this type of credit is supplied.

TRANSPORTATION

The problem of transportation and its cost is a major consideration for the physician starting in practice. Discuss this problem with doctors of long experience and listen carefully to their suggestions. Doctors are usually so busy that they seldom take time out to have their car properly maintained and serviced. The result may be a sudden and expensive major repair. As is often the case, the large repair bill usually occurs at a most inconvenient financial time. Each person must choose the automobile that he prefers and that in his judgment will provide the best and most economical service. Many garages will make an arrangement to keep your car on a regular maintenance schedule and will agree to provide all necessary parts, labor, and service for a fixed sum per month and year. This possibility is worth serious consideration.

Many physicians have found that leasing automobiles at a fixed price per month or per mile is the most economical method of assuring dependable transportation. This usually includes all maintenance costs except gasoline and oil. Leasing agreements usually cover fire and theft insurance but not public liability or property damage, or collision coverage. One of the chief advantages of the leasing method is that all costs are known and measurable and can be accounted for as strictly a business expense.

LOCATION OF THE OFFICE

The location of the office is not always subject to the discretion of the doctor but is governed by zoning laws and available space in existing buildings. It is a foregone conclusion that the best location is in a residential neighborhood. If it is possible to have the office as a part of the doctor's home it is an economical arrangement at the outset, but in the interests of family privacy and happiness a separation of the office facility from the home living area should be made as soon as possible. Parking facilities for patients' cars is a difficult problem in many communities and may become the subject of friction with neighbors.

15

Auxiliary Services

by Ulrich R. Bryner

From the day he enters practice every physician constantly
seeks an answer to the question: How can I run my practice more
efficiently? In other words, how can he provide for the medical
needs of all his patients and give the best possible medical service?

As a physician's practice grows and the demands of his patients
become heavier, he generally finds himself in a never ending race
against the clock. Within the inflexible confines of a 24-hour day
he must maintain the precarious balance between providing for
the needs of his patients and his own physical needs for rest and
relaxation. He must make the most of his time by adopting some
sound and sensible principles of practice management.

MEDICAL ASSISTANTS

The medical assistant is the "front door" to a doctor's practice. A
pleasant, helpful nurse or secretary can be one of a physician's
greatest public relations assets. She can attract patients — and help
him to care for more patients — or she can drive away old patients
and discourage new ones from coming.

The average independent physician today sees 12 per cent more
patients daily than he did in 1948. A 1952 survey of 5000 physicians conducted by the magazine *Medical Economics* (1) revealed
that the physician who employs one or more aides spends 40 per

cent less time per patient than does the doctor who works alone. The survey also showed that doctors with aides put in about the same number of working hours as those without aides, but their daily patient load is 60 per cent higher.

According to the same *Medical Economics* study, three-fourths of the physicians in this country employ one or more full-time aides. Among the medical specialists, with the exception of psychiatrists and neuropsychiatrists, 73 per cent to 90 per cent of the physicians surveyed employed aides. Of doctors employing assistants 65 per cent employed one aide, 23 per cent employed two aides, and 12 per cent employed three or more aides.

Types of Assistants

Every physician who decides to hire a medical assistant must decide what kind of aide he should hire, for she may be a registered nurse, a technician, a medical secretary, a receptionist, or a combination of one or more of these. A registered nurse is a particularly valuable addition to a physician's practice, for she can carry out many routine procedures under his direction, thus allowing him to increase his patient load greatly. It is equally important that an assistant be employed who can not only help with the medical side of the practice, but who can meet the doctor's patients and handle some of the business details.

As early as possible, therefore, an office nurse should be engaged. Because the doctor is then able to see more patients, he may find that he has sufficient income to hire a secretary too. In large practices the staff of assistants may include registered nurses, medical technicians, medical secretaries, and receptionists.

What are the requirements for an office assistant? Because she must deal with the doctor's patients every day, her personality is very important. A pleasant disposition is a necessity, not only for the patient's sake, but for the doctor's sake. She must be able to take the pressures of the physician's office in her stride. And she must be friendly, courteous, and tactful. Intelligence is a prime factor, since the assistant must be efficient and able to assume sufficient authority to handle situations that may arise while the doctor is away. She must know how to cope with anxious patients, and the doctor should be able to depend on her to contact him immediately if he is out of the office when an emergency arises.

The degree of specialized training necessary for an office assistant depends upon the type of work the physician wishes her to do. Some physicians prefer a registered nurse or technician who can, if necessary, be trained to handle business details. Other doctors hire a secretary and train her to assist with routine medical procedures. The personal traits of the individual will largely determine which of these alternatives is followed in a given case.

Selecting the Employee

Since young women who fill the requirements for good medical assistants are not always easy to find, it is a good idea to try the systematic technics developed by personnel experts for hiring an aide.

The first task is to decide exactly what duties the assistant will assume. Is she to be secretary, bookkeeper, office nurse, laboratory technician, receptionist, or a combination of these? When the doctor has analyzed his requirements, he should write out a complete job description. Next, he should try to imagine the kind of person he thinks would fit the job, and put his specifications on paper. Here, in brief, are some suggested steps (2) to follow:

1. Decide exactly what tasks the job entails.

2. Decide what sort of girl is wanted in terms of age, marital status, and education.

3. Enlist the aid of colleagues, friends, schools, employment agencies, and members of the hospital staff in the recruiting process; advertise in newspapers or professional journals for applicants.

4. In interviews, rate applicants on personality, voice, poise, intelligence, self-confidence, education, and ambition.

5. Have applicants fill out a personal history form.

6. Hold final interviews with the best applicant.

7. Get a third-person check by phone from a past employer.

8. If there is still doubt, give likely candidates aptitude tests to evaluate mental ability, clerical skill, and personality.

Such careful screening and testing in the hiring of an aide help the doctor sift out the best candidates. Time and money spent in training a girl who proves to be unfit for her position are unnecessary wastes. Ready-made kits that provide interview guides and necessary forms for applicants can be secured from the Personnel Institute or the Psychological Corporation in New York. Or the physician may prefer to design materials to fit his own needs.

Training the Assistant

Once an assistant is hired, she must be thoroughly trained in the office routine. Her duties and responsibilities should be carefully outlined and procedures for handling any situation that might arise in the office should be explained carefully.

She must be taught the proper methods for dealing with patients and be thoroughly familiarized with any business duties she may have to perform, even if it is necessary for her to take a short course in bookkeeping. In this respect it must be made sure that the initial bookkeeping setup is correct. A number of medical societies today sponsor short courses for medical assistants, and if such a course is held in his locality the physician should certainly encourage his assistant to enroll. Organized groups of medical assistants also do much to further the "professional" education of such aides. The doctor himself should exercise patience during the training period. A new assistant cannot be expected to learn all of the aspects of her position in the first week on the job.

Wages

A busy doctor should pay his aide an average or better than average salary for the community in which he lives. Well-paid assistants are surely happier and more loyal. In 1952 *Medical Economics* reported that the average weekly salary for full-time aides was $54 and that salaries ranged from $48 to $63 in various communities (1, 3).

Valuable employees deserve good wages. No physician should be afraid to increase the salaries of competent help or hesitate to give such Christmas and holiday bonuses as may seem indicated.

HANDLING PATIENT CALLS

At frequent intervals every practicing physician needs to sit down and analyze his own setup, asking himself these questions: Where is the office setup weak? Where will capable assistance help to give more and better medical service? Every improvement in a physician's office facilities and routine adds to his efficiency and helps save precious time. Effective routine in handling patient calls is obviously important.

The Telephone

The telephone is absolutely essential to a physician's practice. Although its ring may become a very unpleasant sound to most doctors, the telephone is the lifeline of the medical profession. When a real emergency call comes over the wire, it must be answered immediately by the physician himself if humanly possible. All other telephone messages should be taken down, and he should call back faithfully as soon as he is free.

Patient Call-backs

Many doctors ask patients to make all phone calls during certain
hours of the day. For example, a doctor may request his patients
to phone him at home between 8 A.M. and 9 A.M. to report on their
condition. Pediatricians find the early morning call especially desirable, since it helps them trace the progress of a sick child and
determine whether or not a house call should be scheduled for
later in the day. Those who practice surgery usually operate in the
morning and would not request calls at this time.

A general practitioner who does a good deal of surgery may
prefer to have his patients report to him by telephone before he
leaves the office around 5 P.M. When the call requires no additional immediate attention, the secretary can leave the message on
the desk so that the doctor can check it when he surveys the other
phone calls that have come in during the day. Patients who request to speak with him should be put through unless he is busy;
if he is, he should call back when he is free. Because of time limitations, many busy practitioners place on the patients themselves
the responsibility of calling back to report on their condition.

It is tremendously important that telephone calls be handled
correctly. From a public relations standpoint, they should be
answered promptly, courteously, and pleasantly. From an efficiency standpoint, they must be taken down completely and correctly. In particular, when the doctor is out of the office and an
emergency call comes in, the assistant should find out who is
calling, the address, the nature of the emergency, directions on
how to reach the patient, the patient's condition, the phone number of the caller, and other details. She never says, "The doctor is
not in." Instead, she says, "The doctor is out right now, but I
think I can reach him. Is it anything urgent?"

Every doctor should keep his office informed of his whereabouts
so that when an emergency does arise, he can be reached quickly
by telephone.

Charging for Telephone Calls

Some physicians believe that it is proper to charge for medical advice given over the telephone. These men also believe that charging for calls discourages excessive telephoning on the part of patients. From a practical as well as a philosophical point of view, there seems to be no logical way of charging for this type of medical service. If a doctor believes that a patient is demanding too much telephone advice, he can suggest an office appointment and examination and honestly tell the patient he has to satisfy himself in regard to the condition. This method effectively curtails patients who make excessive demands on the doctor's time by abusing the telephone privilege. It satisfies the patient and promotes better medical care.

PROVIDING EMERGENCY COVERAGE

Now and then the ringing of the phone alerts the physician to what may be an emergency call requiring immediate attention. Often, however, what appear to be "emergencies" are in reality not emergencies at all. Parents panic when a child becomes ill — and patients often seem to be taking a turn for the worse late at night when the house is quiet. There is a real need for further education of the patient regarding what constitutes a medical emergency. Nevertheless, the majority of such calls — real or fancied emergencies — must be answered by the doctor. Acute illness or even the possibility of such illness should never be diagnosed or treated by telephone.

Many people list overcharging and the inability to get a physician in an emergency as the chief complaints against doctors. (The second complaint, of course, is dependent on what the patient considers to be an "emergency.") Regarding the first complaint, every ethical physician will agree that unnecessary, expensive medical procedures and frank overcharging are inexcus-

able. Most patients gladly accept financial responsibility for the
necessary tests and procedures when they are explained to them.

The Physician's Responsibility

In regard to the second charge, the *Principles of Medical Ethics*
clearly explains the physician's duty in cases of so-called emergency. Says the code: "The physician should respond to any request for his assistance in any emergency or whenever temperate
public opinion expects this service."

No more damaging charge can be placed against the medical
profession than that a physician refused to accept an emergency
plea for medical aid. Furthermore, service is all a physician has
to sell. He must learn how to give satisfaction in dispensing it.
Doctors who have dedicated their lives and energies to the practice of medicine must frequently miss many of the everyday
pleasures of life, such as radio and TV shows, movies and evening
entertainments, in order to be available for these necessary calls
and to render medical service at the time it is required.

No practitioner can be constantly on medical duty, however.
The average doctor cares for his own patients unless he is out of
town, but to handle emergencies that may arise and provide for
the needs of his patients when he is away, he must arrange not
only for night coverage but for week-end and holiday coverage.
He has a responsibility to his patients to make sure that another
physician is ready to care for them when he is not available.

Week-End, Night, and Holiday Coverage

Doctors in solo practice have to resort to a telephone service or
grouping of physicians to cover emergencies. The average physician can't afford to maintain his own 24-hour phone service, but
if all the physicians in a community support one service, the cost
is minor to each one. In such small communities, informal ar-

rangements should be made by physicians to alternate week ends, Wednesdays, Saturdays, and other "days off" to assure complete medical coverage.

In Monongahela, Pennsylvania, for example, five general practitioners have evolved this system for handling emergency calls. On Wednesdays, Sundays, and holidays two of them remain in town to cover any medical problem that might arise. The other three are free from duty. Any fees, regardless of who does the work, go to the man who is the family physician of that patient. Thus, each doctor knows that while he is away, not only are his patients being cared for, but also that he will not endure any financial loss.

Formal Night and Emergency Call Systems

In larger communities county medical societies have set up 24-hour night and emergency telephone-answering services to provide around-the-clock medical coverage. Though these services vary in form, all work on a very similar arrangement. A rotating panel of physicians agrees to handle such calls and provide medical services for persons who cannot reach their family doctor in an emergency or do not have a family physician.

Some of these emergency call programs are carried on through the full-time offices of the county medical society; others are commercial telephone-answering systems that provide special medical emergency call facilities. In small communities the hospital and the medical society join forces to provide continuous emergency medical coverage.

In most cases, the operator who receives an emergency call inquires whether or not the patient has a family physician and attempts to locate him. However, if he is unavailable or if the patient has no family doctor, a member of the emergency call panel is contacted and dispatched. If the patient's doctor was away when the call came in, the emergency panel doctor who accepted the call prepares a report on the patient's condition and the treatment given and returns it to the family doctor.

The Council on Medical Service of the American Medical Association reported in 1953 that "the growth of emergency call plans continues and many county medical societies report this program has been one of the most effective public relations aids of all their society activities. It is estimated that there may be over 800 such systems in operation in 1954. These include most all of the larger societies. Those without formal plans are usually the smaller societies which must depend on informal arrangements by or among individual physicians to provide coverage for patients in the community."

Studies made by individual societies of the calls received in the operation of such emergency call systems indicate that there is little abuse of the service by the public. The majority of the calls answered seem to be either actual emergencies or sufficiently serious to warrant the patient's urgent concern. The main difficulty encountered, according to reports of many societies, is the lack of volunteers from the society membership to handle the calls. In an increasing number of societies this problem is being met by a compulsory duty roster whereby all members not exempt by age or disability take their turn in treating emergencies. Almost all the medical specialty boards now agree that a physician may participate in such emergency plans without endangering his standing as a specialist, since he has a primary responsibility as a physician in cases of emergency.

The first requisite of the successful handling of emergencies in a community of any size is an understanding and co-operative medical profession. Some physician has to make the emergency night call — every physician should co-operate in such programs so that the burden does not fall on the few. The second requisite is a well-defined plan for handling such calls, a plan that is understood and accepted by the public and the co-operating physicians.

SCHEDULING APPOINTMENTS

Reconciling the patients' needs and demands with the doctor's schedule is no easy task. By employing capable assistants, utilizing the telephone more effectively, and joining with other physicians to work out systems to provide around-the-clock medical coverage, the physician can conserve his own time and dispense better medical service. He also can add to his efficiency by running his practice on the basis of the appointment system rather than the hit-or-miss "office hours" basis.

Advantage of Appointment System

Some doctors claim that because of emergencies and other interruptions it is impossible to maintain an appointment schedule. Nevertheless, appointments should be made for office visits if it is at all possible. One of the most oft-heard complaints about medicine today is that people must wait too long to see the doctor. Intelligent scheduling of appointments reduces excessive waiting and eliminates such complaints.

A flexible appointment schedule takes a good deal of the strain off the doctor. When he knows the reception room is full of waiting patients he cannot give the best medical care. One physician reports that if he is aware that his reception room is crowded, he either unconsciously hurries each patient or overcompensates and is unnecessarily deliberate. Furthermore, a large reception room today costs money in terms of rent, heat, light, and furnishings. A doctor who follows the appointment system can cut down on the size of his reception room.

How to Schedule Appointments

The scheduling of appointments is one of the most important tasks that a physician may assign his assistant. It is a duty requiring intelligence, judgment, and an understanding of the doctor's habits and procedures.

Appointments for complete examinations of new patients should, of course, not be scheduled too closely together. Two or three such examinations is probably the maximum that should be scheduled within a given half day, since emergencies are sure to arise. The schedule should be adjusted to fit the individual physician's practice and the needs of the patient on that particular visit. It is also a good idea to allow a fifteen-minute "breather" in the schedule once or twice during the day to allow the physician to catch up if he is running late.

Interruptions in the Appointment Schedule

When an emergency call comes in and the doctor must upset his appointment schedule and leave the office, his assistant should immediately explain the delay to waiting patients and express the doctor's concern over the inconvenience he is causing them. Most patients are understanding; they know that in a personal emergency the doctor would leave his patients and come to their aid.

The medical assistant should give waiting patients an opportunity to make a new appointment or to return later. She should also phone patients with later appointments before they leave home and if possible arrange appointments for another date. Interruptions do upset the appointment schedule, but there are ways of handling such situations without deviating too far from the schedule.

While his nurse or technician is taking a patient's history, carrying out routine weight and height checks, or other routine and laboratory procedures, the busy doctor can supervise the care of those patients requiring only short visits. To give maximum efficiency in the office, all possible routine should be delegated to the aide. She intercepts the doctor's phone calls, screens the mail, and manages the business side of his practice, and also serves as his assistant in the examining room or treatment room.

Coping with Appointment Breakers

The doctor who adopts the appointment system must cope occasionally with the patient who breaks his appointment. Regardless of the reasons why patients do not keep their appointments these cases do occur, and there are several ways a physician can minimize hitches connected with them. Patients who make appointments while in the doctor's office should always be given an appointment card. Cards can be mailed to other patients to remind them of their appointments.

Some physicians and dentists charge for broken appointments. This procedure should seldom be adopted because it upsets and even drives patients away. It may sometimes, however, be used as an effective threat to prevent future broken appointments.

A verbal spanking can be administered to patients who break appointments when they do come into the office, but it is doubtful that these are very effective in reducing future difficulties. One physician suggests that the doctor's assistant compile a list of perennial appointment-breakers. The next day's appointment schedule should be checked against this list. Then the assistant should politely phone previous appointment offenders and remind them that they are expected. The phone call not only flatters the patient, but minimizes failures and helps reduce tardiness.

Evening Office Hours

In some localities doctors hold evening office hours on certain nights during the week. There are advantages to this procedure from the patient's point of view. More men can come to the doctor's office at night, and office hours in the evening increase the number of visits from couples who wish to come to the office together. Women who work regularly in the daytime or are confined at home with youngsters also benefit from evening hours. Transportation and parking problems are reduced at night. From the doctor's standpoint, however, evening hours increase the cost of medical care because house calls must then be made at a later hour. In addition, office help demand higher wages for working at night.

Whether or not a physician holds evening hours still does not alter the fact that once a practice is fairly well established it is best to run it on the appointment basis. *Then the doctor runs his practice — the practice doesn't run him!*

SUMMARY

This goal, which can be attained through efficient practice management, is certainly a desirable one from the physician's standpoint. Utilization of the services of auxiliary personnel, participation in medical programs to provide around-the-clock emergency medical coverage, and the establishment of routine procedures, such as the scheduling of appointments and effective use of the telephone, to facilitate the day-to-day operation of a medical practice, help the physician reach that goal. In the process the physician not only improves the quality of the medical service that he renders and increases the number of patients he can see, but also wins the appreciation and good will of his patients.

REFERENCES

1. City Doctor, Country Doctor; Contributions to Charity; Physicians' Aides. (Report, 7th *Medical Economics* Survey.) *Medical Economics,* April, 1953.
2. Eight Steps in Hiring an Aide. *Medical Economics,* November, 1951.
3. Physicians' Incomes; The High-Income Doctor. (Report, 7th *Medical Economics* Survey.) *Medical Economics,* December, 1952.

16

Office Records

by Bertram T. Uren

SINCE THE PRACTICE of medicine involves both professional service and business procedures, a certain amount of book work is necessary. If it is done in an orderly fashion and not put off until tomorrow, it will quickly be accepted as a part of the normal routine that maintains a practice on an efficient level, to the benefit of doctor as well as patient.

APPOINTMENT BOOK

If patients are to be seen by appointment, an appointment book should be used. Although at the beginning of a practice appointments may be few, it is not advisable to use the day book — the record of patients seen each working day — to list appointments. Patients do break appointments and change the hours. Deletions and erasures should not appear in the day book.

APPOINTMENT CARDS

Appointment cards are an important adjunct to the appointment book and can be used freely, unless the appointment is only a day or so ahead. Some cards are printed with a footnote asking the patient to notify the doctor within 48 or 24 hours if the appointment cannot be kept; the use of such cards is a matter of

choice. Other cards go further and warn that a regular charge
will be made if notification is not received; their use is not advisable, as it would invariably create antagonism. Only an older
doctor with an outstanding reputation could, were he so minded,
use these cards without thought of the patient's reaction.

A broken appointment may be due to circumstances beyond the
patient's control that have made cancellation impossible. To build
good will, it would be better to write off the appointment time.
However, if the patient breaks a second appointment, he should
be warned not to do so again. If a patient, after breaking an appointment, fails to make another, do not write him or send him
a card saying that an appointment has been made for such and
such a time, and asking him to let you know if it will be convenient. Some patients consider that this is drumming up business. It is not good policy.

DAY BOOK

The day book is a record of patients seen each working day,
including charges for service, and payments. As it is also a record
for tax purposes, entries should be legible and accurate. It does
not have to be a book printed for the purpose. A year book, if
the pages for the days are lined, will do. Ruled columns for
charges and payments are not necessary.

It should be used in such a manner that its contents are not
public property. If the doctor has a secretary, when the book is
not in use it should be kept in her desk drawer; entries should
not be made when a patient is present. Its use by a doctor who has
no such assistant is not bound by any set rule except that the contents are confidential. Complete entries may have to be made in
between seeing patients, or after office hours.

For a record of patients seen at the office, enter the name of the
patient, then the charge, then the payment, if any:

John Applegate	$5.00	$ 5.00
Harold McNulty	5.00	————
Thomas Prince	8.00	5.00
Mrs. H. B. Larson	5.00	30.00
William Jennings	NC	NC

Thus, according to the record, John Applegate owes nothing, Harold McNulty owes $5, Thomas Prince owes $3, Mrs. H. B. Larson paid the charge of $5 and $25 she owed, and William Jennings was not charged.

If the patient is the wife, or a son, daughter, or relative of the head of the family, for an accurate record enter the name of the head of the family:

Miss Mary Talbot	$5.00	$5.00
(Arthur Talbot)		

If a wife's given name is preferred, for a more personalized form, do not omit the name of the head of the family:

Mrs. Gertrude Nevins	$5.00	$5.00
(Harry Nevins)		

To maintain a record of patients seen outside the office, thereby keeping a check on sources of income, leave a space between the entries for patients seen at the office and those for patients who receive service at a hospital, or who are seen at their homes or a hospital.

The record of payments received by mail, or from a person who is not a patient for the day, should also be separated from the record of patients seen at the office:

Charles Widmer	*Mail*	$20.00
T. H. Skolnik	*Hand*	25.00

When a charge is to be paid, in whole or in part, by compensation, hospital plan, or another person, the source of payment should be clearly indicated:

Martin Andrews $150.00 *Comp.*
Tom Smith   80.00 *Blue Cross $60.00*
                               Patient   *20.00*
Arthur Goldsmith   65.00 *Carry Corp.*
                               1256 Drew Lane
                               City

Circle the charge as a warning not to bill incorrectly.

PATIENT'S RECORD

This is a record of the service to the patient, with the date and
to whom given. It should be written or typed on a file card (4 by
6 or 5 by 8 inches) or on letter-size paper and subsequently filed.
Care should be exercised to make the record complete; no record
of minor service given to a new patient should be omitted, in the
belief that he may not return for further service. A record may
become part of a legal action, or may be required for future reference.

For a family record, enter the head of the family as the patient.
When a member of the family receives service, enter his or her
name immediately following the date and preceding the description of the service.

When the card system is used, the patient's record can be kept
on a separate card, or it can be combined with the account record.
This combination card allows space for recording the charge, payment, and balance. Some doctors prefer the combination card, as
it eliminates having to prepare and file two cards. Other doctors
prefer the two-card system, as this separates the service from the
charge. When used in front of a patient who owes a bill, the
separate patient's record does not serve as a reminder that, while
recording the service, the doctor is perhaps also thinking he
should record payment instead of waiting to receive it from billing. Furthermore, the combination card, as part of a legal action,

would show payments for services, which is a confidential matter between doctor and patient. As a practice grows, cards to be filed may be left on the doctor's or the secretary's desk, so that patients coming or going would be able to see them. Although the description of service may be unreadable, the patient's name and pattern of paying can be taken in at a glance — a possible forerunner for gossip detrimental to a neighborhood practice.

Before selecting either type of card, it may be wise to consult some of the older men to get the benefit of their long experience. Cards printed especially for general practitioners and for some of the specialties are frequently inadequate. Many doctors complain that the fronts of these cards are wasted when headings are not applicable to a patient's service requirements, or are insufficient when applicable, particularly for positive findings. And with certain of the specialties, the complaint is that the cards are not up to date for recording positive and negative findings. Consequently, these doctors use their own cards, chiefly 5 by 8 inches, lined front and back. The only printing is the headings on the front: *Name, Address, Telephone, Referred By,* and *Remarks.* Some doctors have nothing printed on the card. Some members of the specialties have the cards printed for positive and negative findings, according to their personal preferences.

ACCOUNT RECORD

This is a record of the patient, date of service, charge, payment, and balance, entered on a file card and subsequently filed. Or it may be entered on a loose-leaf sheet and filed in a ledger. It is also a reference for billing. It can be combined with the patient's record and the entries made following the complete record of service; for this, use a card 5 by 8 inches, printed front and back:

DATE	DESCRIPTION OF SERVICE	CHARGE	PAID	BALANCE

Or use a separate card — a letter-size patient's record always requires the separate card. This should be 3 by 5 or 4 by 6 inches, printed front and back:

DATE	SERVICE	CHARGE	PAID	BALANCE

Under *Service* should be entered the name of the patient when he is not the head of the family, and abbreviations or other indication of the type of service, such as "OV" (office visit), "OV inj." (office visit plus injection), or "surgery." This facilitates itemizing first bills. Data for this card — the patient's name, charge, and payment — can be taken from the day book, and the address of a new patient from the patient's record. Service may be indicated by the charge; when it is not, it can be taken from the patient's record.

A card that does not have a balance column should not be used. Omission of this column means extra billing effort in time required to total the amount due. Also, it is important to keep the balance up to date, showing whether "nothing" or "something" is due:

DATE	DES. OF SERVICE, OR ABBR.	CHARGE	PAID	BALANCE
Enter	*Enter*	$15.00	———	$15.00
Enter None		———	10.00	5.00
Enter	*Enter*	10.00	15.00	———
Enter	*Enter*	25.00	10.00	15.00

Lines (———) always indicate that there was no charge because there was no service, or that nothing was paid at the time of service, or that there was no balance after payment.

Compensation or a medical plan that pays the doctor in full should be accurately recorded:

Date	Des. of Service, or Abbr.	Charge	Paid	Balance
Enter	*Enter*	*$125.00*		*Comp.*
		or		
Enter	*Enter*	*125.00*		*Blue Cross*

When the medical plan pays only in part, bill the patient for the full amount if payment is not made before the first of the month:

Date	Des. of Service, or Abbr.	Charge	Paid	Balance
Enter	*Enter*			
	(Blue Cross $80.00)	*$125.00*	———	*$125.00*
Enter	*None Paid by Blue Cross*	———	*$80.00*	*45.00*
Enter	*None Paid by Patient*	———	*45.00*	———

When payment is to be made by another person and the patient owes a balance when that charge is paid, record the payment and balance in this manner:

Date	Des. of Service, or Abbr.	Charge	Paid	Balance
Enter	*Enter*	*$50.00*	*J. Henry & Sons*	
			42 Warren St.	
			City	
Enter	*Enter*	*15.00*	———	*$15.00*
Enter	*None Paid by J. Henry*	———	*$50.00*	*15.00*

Do not fail to make a card for a patient who pays, no matter how small the charge. A charge entered in the day book must show on an account record.

If an adequate card cannot be found already printed, a printer will order cards lined on both sides and print them according to your specifications.

FILING

Case numbers are not necessary and would require a double filing system. When filing a patient's name, the more practical system is the first name first ("Henry Adam") rather than the last name first ("Adam, Henry").

Patient's Record

Letter-size patients' records should have an individual folder for each patient and should be filed under "Patients." Some doctors file a new patient's record under "Miscellaneous" and use the individual folder only when the patient returns for further service. Card-form patients' records that are not combined with the account records should be filed under "Patients." Card records that are combined with the account records should be filed under one of two groups, "Paid Accounts" and "Unpaid Accounts," in order to facilitate billing.

Account Record

Cards should be filed under one of two groups, "Paid Accounts" and "Unpaid Accounts." Loose-leaf sheets should also be filed in the ledger under one of the two groups.

Compensation — Medical Plan — Clinic Reports

These can be filed in individual folders marked with the patient's name, or in special folders for "Compensation," "Medical Plan," or "Clinic Reports." When filing in a special folder, file alphabetically; do not merely open the folder and insert the report haphazardly.

DISCUSSING BILLS

When he sees a patient for the first time, it may be difficult for the doctor to know what to say or do relative to the charge. When a patient asks, "Shall I pay you now, or will you send me a bill?" the doctor's best answer, with friendly emphasis on the first few words, is, "Well, you can save me the trouble of acting the part of a bookkeeper, or I can bill you if you prefer." If the doctor has a secretary, instead of suggesting that the patient see her, the doctor may say, ". . . save Miss Doe the trouble of bookkeeping, and she will appreciate it, or I . . ." When a patient says, "Please send me a bill," the only reply should be in co-operative agreement. When a patient says nothing about the bill, it is more profitable, for good will, to say nothing in turn, and bill for the first of the month. This also applies to house calls.

The charge may invite discussion, particularly when it is fairly large; payment in a lump sum in such a case may seem questionable, and the doctor may be agreeable to part payments within a reasonable time. Discussion of the charge is far removed from commercialism when the doctor is making sincere effort to help the patient meet his obligation. The doctor might say, "My bill will be $250. Now I know that is a lot of money for you. I don't want to add to your worries, but as you know your finances better than I, I am certain we can come to some arrangement that will not make matters worse for you." After an arrangement has been made, the patient should not be asked to sign an agreement. If after the discussion the patient is shown up as a dead beat, he will represent the minority. For it is an established fact that the majority of patients who owe medical bills are honest.

BILLING

Bill according to the balance shown on the account record, either the separate card or the card combined with the patient's record. A set rule for billing is to mail bills to reach patients on the first of the month, and of every necessary month thereafter. Some doctors postpone until the next month charges incurred toward the end of the month, the twenty-fifth, twenty-sixth, or twenty-seventh. This allows several days to prepare bills. Also, not billing for services performed almost the day before the bill is rendered is good psychology.

In order to ascertain whether the rule of first of the month billing is rigidly applied each month, leave a space at the bottom across the front and back of the account record for entering the date bills are sent; allowing space on the combination card is a matter of choice. The reason why some doctors are the last to be paid, if they are paid at all, is that they have ignored the billing rule. Billing on different days each month, or omitting bills for one month or more, is hit and miss billing, which, by creating the impression that the doctor can afford to wait, invites patients to delay paying.

Further, bills should be addressed to the person legally responsible for payment; they should bear the patient's given name and not "Mr.," "Mrs.," or "Miss Doe," which is lacking in courtesy. A bill for extra charges or for consultation should be fully explained to the patient, in order to avoid possible controversy.

The first bill should be itemized. This gives the patient a check on services and charges. Billing for "services rendered," when there were many charges, does not present a true picture; the patient sees only the total of the bill. The extra effort of itemizing will pay extra dividends. The following are examples of itemized billing:

Itemized billing for several identical charges:

House Calls (12)
January 2, 3, 4, 6, 8, 10, 10,
11, 12, 13, 14, 15 $84.00

Itemized billing for average charges:

January 18	OV	$ 5.00
" 19	HC	7.00
" 21	OV X ray	20.00
		$32.00

In itemized billing under the head of the family, list the members of the family; not listing them would indicate that the head of the family received the service:

January 4	Mary OV		$ 5.00
" 5	Mrs. Talbot HC		7.00
" 10	OV inj.		8.00
			$20.00

Billing for charges that were itemized in the last bill should be shown as "previously rendered." New charges during the month should be itemized:

Previously rendered	$46.00
January 8, 8, 10 HC	21.00
	$67.00

If part of the itemized bill was paid during the month, it should be shown as "balance" and not "previously rendered."

In billing for a charge that includes postoperative care, always show the number of weeks or months:

January 18   *Surgery* $250.00
including 3 months'
postoperative care

In billing for compensation, give the patient's case number and the name of his employer. Itemize in full with no abbreviations, and keep a duplicate in the file; such bills have been known to go astray. Subsequent monthly bills are not necessary. Wait for payment. If it is not made within a reasonable time, an inquiry is in order. If, after the first bill, additional service is given, the bill will be for that charge; it should not refer to the previous bill rendered. The doctor should exercise care to obtain authorization from the insurance carrier to give further service; his charge should conform to the schedule of allowances, and he should make reports — particularly progress reports — as required by the carrier. When the doctor is in doubt about procedure, the carrier will prove helpful.

Before billing in an accident case, it is wise to have a thorough understanding about the bill. If it is to be "legal" and payment is to be made when the case is settled, the patient should arrange with his lawyer to protect the doctor's interests.

WHEN BILLS FAIL

A medical bill, unlike a commercial bill, is usually incurred with no agreement regarding payment. It is a reminder of the debt, not a request for payment. Therefore payment from billing alone may be entirely dependent upon what the patient considers is a reasonable time, or it may be based solely upon his experience with the billing systems of other doctors. In some cases he may simply wait until payment is requested — or, in the minority of cases, until it is demanded.

There are too many human factors involved to set a limit on the number of bills that should be sent. However, with an average account, a minimum of three bills should be sent before deciding whether to continue bills or to request payment. The first step in making the request is a footnote on one, two, or three bills, such as:

Please accept this as a reminder that payment will be appreciated. Thank you.

or

> *If there is any reason why payment cannot be made, please communicate with me.*

If there is no response to the first step, do not return to bills. Wide experience has shown that a second step must follow. This should be either a telephone call by the doctor's assistant, who might ask, "Is there any reason for your not replying to the footnoted bills?" or an amicable letter — not a collection letter demanding payment — such as:

> *My office has brought to my attention your failure to reply to the footnoted bills regarding your account of $50.*
>
> *As I am most eager to co-operate with you, I shall appreciate your communicating with me within the next few days.*
>
> *Thanking you, I am*

If the patient does not reply, a second amicable letter (sent in a plain envelope) two weeks later often proves effective in place of the collection letter:

> *I am wondering whether your failure to reply to my letter of [date] is an oversight, or whether there is any particular reason why payment should not be made at this time.*
>
> *If you will let me hear from you, I am confident we can arrange liquidation to our mutual satisfaction.*

If there is still no response, the collection letter (also sent in a plain envelope) can be used without loss of good will:

> *I am sorry to have to inform you that [if your account of $50.00 is not paid in full,] [if a satisfactory arrangement for payment of your account of $50.00 is not made,] within seven days from today's date, I shall place it in the hands of my [attorney.] [collector.]*
>
> *I hope you will make this action on my part unnecessary.*

If there has been no response ten days later, place the bill for collection. The action will be justified.

COLLECTION AGENCIES

Do not choose a collection agency, if one has to be used, that retains the right to keep an account as long as it pleases. Another agency may be able to collect. Difficult accounts require persistent effort, and collection will not be made if, after writing a few letters, the first type of agency merely files the account.

Long years of personal experience covering many thousands of patients who owed medical bills have shown unequivocally that placing on account for collection, after amicable procedure has failed, creates no ill will for the doctor, even when he is located in a residential area, and even if he unwittingly engages a hardboiled agency. The only time that there is loss of good will is when the doctor violates a fundamental collection principle by demanding payment instead of first requesting it. Antagonism is created, for the patient feels that he was not given a chance to pay in a decent manner and that he was not met halfway.

17

Accounting Practices — The Income Tax

by Paul Gitlin

BOOKS OF ACCOUNT

THE IMPORTANCE of the keeping of proper books of account by any professional man cannot be sufficiently stressed.

For tax purposes the keeping of adequate records is obligatory, and while no prescribed system of accounting is defined, a taxpayer is required to maintain "such accounting records as will enable him to make a return of his true income." These records should be kept in sufficient detail to "establish the gross income and the deductions, credits and other matters" required to be shown on the tax return. When the taxpayer has kept no records, or maintained inadequate or incorrect records, the Commissioner of Internal Revenue is permitted by law to compute the tax by such method as will clearly reflect income. In many cases in which inadequate records have been kept, or none at all, the taxpayer's net income is determined by comparing his net worth at the beginning and close of the tax year, including all bank deposits made during the year, without permitting him to make any deductions. In addition, negligence penalties may be levied against such a taxpayer, as was done in a recent case involving a doctor.

Apart from the legal requirements for keeping adequate books of account, the physician should realize that in order to conduct his practice successfully he must keep track of his income and expenses. His cash receipts and disbursements should be properly accounted for, his charge patients properly and promptly billed, and at the end of the year he should be able to determine whether his practice is profitable.

The amount of time devoted to keeping records during the year will be more than amply compensated for by savings in taxes and in time consumed in the preparation of the tax return for such year.

What Records Should Be Kept?

A taxpayer may use either the cash basis or accrual basis method of keeping books, but most professional men should and do use the cash basis method, since it is the simpler of the two and more properly reflects income and expense.

Under the cash basis method, items of income are not included until they are actually received, and expenses incurred are not deducted until actually paid. Thus, at the end of the year, accounts receivable from charge patients are not included in income for the year, and laboratory bills and other expenses unpaid at such time are not deducted from income for the year. However, rent and insurance premiums prepaid must be allocated over the period to which they apply.

Although many types of records are kept, more or less successfully, it is suggested that a professional man employing the cash basis method should keep the following records of account:

Daily Outside Calls

This record is used for listing all outside calls made during each day, whether the patient pays a fee or has it charged to him. For this purpose a small notebook ruled as shown will suffice. Each page of this record should cover only a single day. At the end of each day the entries should be transferred to the daily collections and charges record.

DAILY OUTSIDE CALLS BOOK			DATE	
PATIENT	ADDRESS	CHARGE		CASH RECEIVED
John Jones	54 Elm St.			5 00
Will Brown	24 Oak Ave.	15 00		
Helen Smith	11 Broadway			10 00

Daily Collections and Charges

This record combines all daily cash receipts and charges for professional services, whether for office visits or outside calls. All entries in the charge column are posted to the debit side of the patient's account in the patients' ledger, and all entries in the

DAILY COLLECTIONS AND CHARGES BOOK				DATE	
OFFICE VISITS					
PATIENT	ADDRESS	CASH RECEIVED	CHARGE		PAYMENT ON ACCOUNT
Tom Brown	12 Ford St.	10 00			
Paul Peters	15 Broadway		15 00		10 00
Irene Johnson	115 Henry Ave.		25 00		
Harold Cane	185 Park Ave.	10 00			
OUTSIDE CALLS					
John Jones	54 Elm St.	5 00			
Will Brown	24 Oak Ave.		15 00		
Helen Smith	11 Broadway	10 00			

payment on account column to the credit side. Remittances received through the mail are entered in the payment on account column.

Each page of the daily collections and charges record should cover only one day. At the end of each day only the items entered in the cash received and payment on account columns are totaled; on the sample page $35 is the total for cash received and $10 is the total for payment on account. The final total of $45 is recorded in the cash receipts book. Since these books are maintained on the cash basis method, the total charges for the day are not treated as an item of income.

A looseleaf notebook may be used to maintain this record.

Patients' Ledger

The purpose of this ledger is to maintain a current record of charge accounts so that accurate and prompt billings may be made to patients each month. The preparation and mailing of these statements can be done by the secretary or office nurse.

This ledger may consist of a card file or looseleaf sheets and should be posted daily from the daily collections and charges record. The balance column may be used after each posting or for striking a balance at the end of each month.

PATIENTS' LEDGER

Name: Helen Smith		Residence: 11 Broadway				
Phone: 2-4287		Business: % J. Jones, Inc.				
Symbols: C = Consultation V = Call S = Surgery						
19 —	SERVICE	CHARGES	CREDITS	BALANCE		REMARKS
Feb. 10	C	10 00		10 00		
Mar. 5	V	15 00	15 00	10 00		
15	S	125 00	35 00	100 00		

Cash Receipts Book

This book consists of lined journal sheets containing an explanation column and 6 analysis columns. A looseleaf book may also be use for this purpose; in fact, one looseleaf book, properly indexed, may be used for all the books of account.

Entries in the cash receipts book are made daily from the record of daily collections and charges. Note that these entries consist only of cash receipts; charge items are not considered.

The explanation column is used to describe the income posted in analysis columns 4, 5, and 6 (nonprofessional income). Column 1 records the total income received each day from all sources; column 3 covers professional income and should be the same as the total amount shown each day in the daily collections and charges record. Column 2 records deposits made in your bank.

At the end of each month the various columns in the cash receipts book are totaled. The totals of analysis columns 1 and 2 should be the same; the sum of the totals of the remaining columns should equal the totals of either column 1 or 2. These totals are then posted to the summary cash receipts book.

CASH RECEIPTS BOOK							
19 —	EXPLANATION	NET CASH	DEPOSITS	PROF. INCOME	INTEREST INCOME	DIVIDENDS INCOME	OTHER INCOME
Jan. 2	Note – J. Smith	250 00		185 00	65 00		
3	U. S. Steel	140 00	390 00	90 00		50 00	

Summary Cash Receipts Book

This book of account is composed of entries made once a month from the cash receipts book. It consists of one sheet for each year, with a month column and 5 analysis columns. (Note that the headings of the analysis columns correspond with columns 3, 4, 5 and 6 of the cash receipts book.) At the end of each year these columns are totaled, and the totals are used to report gross income from various sources on the income tax return.

Thus the final result of the year's activity, in terms of gross income from all sources, is readily available by the proper maintenance of records.

We now turn to the books necessary to keep track of expenses incurred during the year.

SUMMARY CASH RECEIPTS BOOK					
19 __	PROF. INCOME	ITEM	INTEREST INCOME	DIVIDENDS INCOME	OTHER INCOME
Jan.					
Feb.					
Mar.					

Cash Disbursement Book

Wherever possible, all payments of expense items should be made only by check, since payment in this fashion affords a permanent record of all disbursements. In addition, receipted bills should be obtained and preserved when such payments are made. The opening of charge accounts with the various tradesmen is advised, including the local gas station, since payments on these accounts need to be made only once a month and cash payments are eliminated.

The cash disbursements book is made up of journal sheets containing an explanation column and 19 analysis columns. Entries in this book should be made from the stubs in your checkbook. At the time a check is issued all pertinent information should be entered on the stub, including the account to be charged.

The amount of each check and the date issued is entered in the net cash column and then posted to the appropriate expense column to the right. The name of the payee is entered in the explanation column. Note that all the columns refer to particular items of expense except analysis columns 18 and 19, which can be used for miscellaneous expense items.

Thus on the sample sheet the amount paid to Surgical, Inc., is charged to medical supplies. The check issued to Mary Jones, the office nurse, represents her net salary after deducting withholding and social security taxes. When you forward the amount withheld and your own contribution to social security to the Director of Internal Revenue, the amount of such payment will

CASH DISBURSEMENT BOOK

19 —	EXPLANATION	NET CASH	OFFICE SALARIES	OFFICE SUPPLIES	LABORATORY EXPENSE	RENT
Jan 2	Surgical, Inc.	49 50			49 50	
5	Mary Jones	39 85	39 85			
6	Con. Edison	15 87				

MEDICAL SUPPLIES	HEAT, LIGHT & POWER	LAUNDRY	AUTOMOBILE	INSURANCE	TELEPHONE	REPAIRS
	15 87					

TAXES	INTEREST, BANK CHARGES	ENTER-TAINMENT	PERSONAL	DUES & SUBSCRIPT.	ACCT. & LEGAL EXP.	SUNDRY	
						ITEM	AMOUNT

be allocated between the office salaries column and the taxes column. The withholding taxes are treated as office salaries.

This book need not be maintained daily, but entries should be made at the end of each month. After the last check is issued for each month, the analysis of petty cash expenditures is made and entered. The various columns are then totaled and the totals entered in the summary cash disbursement book.

Petty Cash Book

Inevitably during the course of the month certain payments are made by cash, either by reason of the nature of the transaction or because the amounts to be paid are small. However, in the course of a year such payments may add up to sizable sums, so a petty cash fund is set up to keep a record of them. The fund is set up and replenished by a check made out to the order of

PETTY CASH BOOK

19 __	EXPLANATION	RECEIPTS	PAYMENTS	MEDICAL	GENERAL	SUNDRY ITEM	AMOUNT
Jan 2	Check #562	50 00					
5	Gasoline		8 57			Auto	8 57
6	Newspapers		3 50			Mag.+Period.	3 50
10	Med. Supplies		17 52	17 52			
15	Clean. Supplies		2 50		2 50		
20	Postage		5 00			Print.+Stat.	5 00
31	Gasoline		5 22			Auto	5 22
		50 00	42 31	17 52	2 50		22 29
	Balance		7 69				
		50 00	50 00				
31	Balance	7 69					
31	Check #612	42 31					

petty cash, which is then cashed. *Under no circumstances should the fund be replenished by cash received from patients or other sources.*

As payments are made from the fund, which can be kept in a metal box by the office nurse, they are recorded in the payments column and the amounts extended to the special column for each type of expense. The sundry column is used for items that have no special column.

At the end of the month an analysis is made of such expenditures and entered in the appropriate columns in the cash disbursement book.

The petty cash fund is usually replenished by restoring the

SUMMARY CASH DISBURSEMENT BOOK						
19 __	OFFICE SALARIES	OFFICE SUPPLIES	LABORATORY EXPENSE	RENT	MEDICAL SUPPLIES	HEAT, LIGHT & POWER
Jan.						
Feb.						
Mar.						

LAUNDRY	AUTOMOBILE	INSURANCE	TELEPHONE	REPAIRS	TAXES	INTEREST, BANK CHARGES

ENTER-TAINMENT	PERSONAL	DUES & SUBSCRIPT.	ACCT. & LEGAL EXP.	SUNDRY	
				ITEM	AMOUNT

fund to its original amount by a check of the exact amount of petty cash disbursements at the time the check is drawn. Thus on the sample page a check of $42.31 was issued at the end of the month to restore the fund to its original figure, $50.00.

Summary Cash Disbursement Book

This book consists of entries made once a month from the cash disbursement book, and the analysis columns correspond exactly with those of that book, except that the net cash column is omitted. At the end of the year the columns of the summary cash disbursement book are totaled and the resulting figures are used in the preparation of the income tax return.

Here too the entire year's expense activity can be easily determined without waste of time, and because record of expense is important in tax savings there is less likelihood of losing any benefits due.

Record of Depreciable Assets

A record of depreciable assets used in the profession should be maintained, since a certain amount of depreciation may be deducted each year as an item of expense.

When an asset to be used in the profession is first acquired, an entry should be made containing a description of the assets, and its cost, date of acquisition, and estimated useful life. At the end

RECORD OF DEPRECIABLE ASSETS		YEAR: 1954			
DESCRIPTION	DATE ACQUIRED	COST		USEFUL LIFE	DEPREC. IN PRIOR YRS.
X-ray machine	6/30/53	1750	00	10 yrs.	262 50
Dodge sedan (90% bus.)	1/1/52	2600	00	5 yrs.	1040 00

of each year a computation is made of the amount of depreciation, based on the useful life of the item. This information is then
entered on the income tax return in the appropriate schedule.
(See discussion of depreciation later in this chapter.)

Payroll Book

Since certain reports must be filed with reference to employees
and taxes must be withheld, a payroll book should be maintained.
Entries in this book should show the name, address, and social
security number of each employee; the total amount paid in
wages to each; the date of payment and the period covered; and
the taxes or other deduction from wages and the net amount
paid. The cumulative totals for each employee during the previous quarter will furnish the necessary information for the
preparation of Form 941, the employers' quarterly tax return.

A payroll book may be purchased at a stationery store.

INCOME TAX (ITEMS OF INCOME AND EXPENSE)

In order to maintain his books of account so that they will be
available for income tax purposes, a professional man should
know which items are those of income and which are those of
expense. The following discussion will deal only with income
and expense arising from the professional activities, since space
will not permit the coverage of all income and expense.

Professional Income

All payments received from patients, whether in the form of
cash or check, are treated as income at the time of receipt. Should
a patient's check be returned by the bank because of lack of
funds the amount is dropped from income until it is later paid.
If the sum is never paid it does not become a bad debt for tax

purposes, since under the cash basis of keeping books such a sum is never treated as an item of income; this applies equally to charge patients who do not pay their bills.

Ordinarily, gifts received from patients, such as those made during the Christmas season, may not be included in income, but should a patient out of gratitude pay more than he was billed, the additional payment is an item of income, since it is connected with the services rendered.

When fees are paid by patients in the form of services or goods, either for office or personal use, the services or goods received are treated as items of income at their fair market value.

Referral Income and Expense

The acceptance or payment of referral fees is a violation of rules prescribed by local and national medical societies; moreover, definite tax consequences may result from such transactions. In all cases, referral income is taxable as ordinary professional income. The United States Supreme Court has recently ruled that payment for referral may or may not be deductible as a business expense, depending on whether such payment is contrary to "sharply defined national or state policies the frustration of which may, as a matter of law, preclude the deductibility of an expense" of this type. Even when specific state legislation forbids payment of referral fees but such practice exists, the referrer must include the receipt of the fee in income; however, the referee may *not* deduct such payment as an item of expense.

Professional Expense

Professional expense is such expense as is "ordinary and necessary" in the conduct of a practice. An expense need not be a recurring item in order to be ordinary; it suffices that the item is one that is common in conducting the practice. If the expense is appropriate and aids in the conduct of the practice, it is treated as necessary.

Substantial tax savings may be accomplished by keeping proper records of expense and knowing which items may be treated as professional expense items, since these are reflected in the income tax return as *deductions* from gross income.

To illustrate, an unmarried practitioner who reports $12,300 taxable income (after expenses and personal exemption of $600) pays a tax of $3529, based on 1954 and 1955 tax rates. Failing to deduct $300 of business expense increases the tax by $129, since the tax on $12,000 is $3400.

Another advantage of keeping close track of items of expense is that in years when his income is high, if the physician's records are up to date, outstanding bills may be paid before the end of the year to minimize tax impact on the high income. Conversely, expense may be high in a given year and income low, so it may pay to let the outstanding bills run into the following year, when income may be higher.

The following discussion of particular items of expense parallels Schedule C of the federal income tax return on which professional expense is entered as "other business deductions."

Salaries and Wages

The total amount paid during the taxable year to a nurse, office assistant, or other professional employee is a deductible business expense. Included in this amount is the weekly withholding made on such an employee's salary. Contributions made as an employer toward social security are not reported here.

Wages paid to a member of a taxpayer's family are deductible, provided services were actually performed and such services were related to the conduct of the practice.

If payments are made to an employee other than by cash, the fair market value of the property given may also be deducted.

Bonuses or Christmas presents given to employees are a salary expense, since they originate out of the employment.

Payments to a cleaning woman or other domestic may be deducted here, provided services were performed relating to office practice. If the office is located in the home and the domestic performs work in both the office and home, an allocation of the payment must be made, based on the amount of time devoted to cleaning of the office.

Office Rent

When the office is not located in the home, the amount deducted is the amount of rent paid to the landlord each year. Brokerage expense incurred in obtaining a lease, or legal fees in connection therewith, must be allocated over the life of the lease.

When the office is located in the home and the physician is a tenant rather than the owner of the premises, the rental must be allocated so that the rental attributable to the running of the office may be determined. Such allocation may be based upon the relative rental value of the part used for home or office, or on the ratio of space used for such purposes.

Any items of the landlord's expense the physician is required to pay, such as taxes on the property, are treated as rent expense. Any repairs made to the premises may also be deducted, and if they apply both to home and office an allocation must be made. Capital improvements made to rented premises, such as erection of office partition walls, must be depreciated over the life of the lease or the life of the improvement, whichever is the shorter period.

Interest Expenses

Interest expense incurred in conducting a practice is fully deductible. Such expense may arise from the purchase of equipment on time or from a bank loan made to equip the office.

When the office is located in the home and interest is paid on a mortgage, an allocation of such expense should be made, based on the ratio of office space to personal space. The balance of the interest may be taken as an interest deduction on page 3 of the income tax return.

Business Tax Expense

During the course of the year many taxes are paid; some of them are wholly related to business, some are mixed, and some are wholly personal.

Those taxes that relate solely to the profession, such as annual license fees, narcotic fees, sales tax on medical equipment, and social security contributions made as an employer, are deductible in full.

Mixed taxes, such as a real property tax when the office is located in the home, must be allocated. The percentage allocated to office use is deducted in Schedule C, the balance may be deducted on page 3 of the tax return as "taxes." Gasoline taxes, when the car is used for both business and pleasure, receive the same treatment.

Excise taxes as a rule are not deductible unless they are connected with business purposes. Therefore only the percentage of telephone and telegraph taxes attributable to the practice may be deducted. The balance of such tax may not be deducted on page 3. The same treatment is accorded to a tax on a railroad ticket.

Occupation taxes, such as local taxes on gross receipts from the practice, are deductible in full.

Depreciation and Obsolescence

Property used in the practice having a useful life of more than one year becomes subject to a depreciation or obsolescence allowance.

Depreciation is a gradual process that extends over a period of years during which capital assets, such as an X-ray machine, sterilizer, office furniture, technical books, medical equipment, and car, wear out. Obsolescence occurs when a piece of equipment becomes out of date because of technical advances or legislation banning its use, so that such equipment has no further value. In either case a deduction on the tax return is permitted, and in the case of obsolescence a shorter useful life is accepted in determining the allowance to be taken.

Useful life of a particular piece of equipment must be ascertained before a depreciation schedule is made up. The Treasury Department has stated that as a general rule the useful life of "professional libraries is 30 years, while the life of scientific equipment used by dentists, doctors, etc. is usually 10 years." Factors that may lessen the period of useful life of such equipment are excessive use, climatic conditions, or purchase of second-hand equipment.

When on the basis of the physician's experience equipment is known to have a useful life of less than 10 years, the manufacturer should be requested to note this fact on the bill. When secondhand equipment is purchased, the length of time it had been used should be ascertained and its condition on purchase noted, so that the balance of its useful life can be determined.

To the extent that professional equipment may have salvage value, before a depreciation deduction is made, such value should be subtracted from its cost. Thus if a new X-ray unit costs $1750 and its salvage value after 10 years is estimated to be $150, the annual depreciation deduction will be $160 (the difference between $1750 and $150, divided by 10).

With reference to depreciation of buildings (when the office is located in the home or used solely for the practice) the factors involved are location and physical condition of the structure. Ordinarily, when a building is of good construction and properly maintained, the useful life of the structure if of brick is 50 years, and if of frame construction, 40 years. When the office is in the home, only that part of the depreciation allowable to business use may be deducted.

In determining the amount of depreciation to be taken on an automobile, a useful life of 4 to 5 years may be assumed, depending on the type of practice in which it is employed, conditions of roads in the area, weather conditions, and the type of car. When the car is used for both business and pleasure, an allocation of depreciation must be made and only the part attributable to business use may be deducted. In order to justify the allocation to be made, it would be advisable to maintain and preserve mileage records for an average week to determine the amount of such mileage used for both purposes.

Situations will arise during a practice where it will be necessary to consider replacement of old equipment or an automobile. Normally this may be done by way of trade-in, where the old equipment plus cash is turned over to the dealer. Sometimes the old equipment may be sold to a secondhand dealer for cash and new equipment purchased from another dealer. There are important tax considerations that may determine which method will be more profitable, and in the event such disposal is being considered, an accountant or attorney should first be consulted.

Repairs

Another deductible item taken on the tax return is the cost of repairs made during the year. Repairs are usually made to keep property in good working order, and are to be distinguished from improvements, which prolong the life of the property. An improvement is the subject of a depreciation allowance to be taken over the useful life of the improvement; a repair is deductible in full in the year paid.

Items of repair that may be deducted are painting of the outside and inside of a building, and plumbing and electrical repairs.

Items to be treated as improvements are installation of new roofs
and replacement of heating apparatus, old cooking equipment, or
an old sink or air conditioner.

Note that in either case, when the office is located in the
home, an allocation must be made to determine the amount attributable to business needs.

Other Business Expense

There are many items of expense that do not fall into special
categories; these items may be lumped into a miscellaneous
grouping identified as "other business expense." Among these
items are:

Professional dues. These would include dues paid to local and
national medical societies as well as any excise tax charged on
such dues. Should the doctor join local groups such as Kiwanis
or a chamber of commerce for business reasons, his membership
dues may be deducted.

Technical journals, magazines. The full cost of technical journals and of newspapers and magazines for the waiting room
may be deducted. Note, however, that technical books have a
useful life longer than one year and must be depreciated.

Legal and accounting fees. Fees paid to an attorney or accountant for services relating to the practice are deductible in
full. Note that the charge for services not related to production
of income may not be deducted. If an attorney or accountant has
performed work of business and personal nature, the charge for
each type of service should be itemized on the bill.

Insurance expense. The cost of insurance premiums relating to
professional coverage may be deducted. Items that relate to personal expense, such as life insurance premiums, may not be deducted.

Items of professional insurance expense are those relating to
automobile, fire, liability, malpractice, theft, radium, forgery,

fidelity, and accounts receivable premiums. Note that when the same policy covers business and personal needs, an allocation of the premium cost must be made. Allocation must also be made when a lump sum is paid for three-year coverage; only the amount attributable to a particular year may be deducted for that year.

Medical and office supplies. The cost of supplies used in the practice may be deducted in full. Since a physician is engaged in selling services rather than supplies, he need not maintain an inventory of unused supplies. Make certain that payments for supplies are made by check and that paid bills are preserved to justify the deduction of the cost of such items.

Entertainment expense. A reasonable amount of the cost of entertainment connected with the practice may be deducted. Such expense must be "ordinary and necessary," as noted above. Expense of this nature must have some connection with the practice rather than be incurred with the hope that professional income will result.

Accurate records for this type of expense, including the names of the guests, must be maintained, since recent announcements by the Treasury Department indicate that entertainment expense will be scrutinized very carefully in the future.

Telephone and telegraph expense. The monthly phone bill attributable to the practice, including the excise tax is deductible in full. Run a record for a test day to determine the amounts of this charge attributable to personal and business use. The monthly charge for a telephone answering service is also deductible.

Traveling expense. The cost of trips away from home to attend medical conventions is deductible in full. This includes such items as railroad fare, lodging, meals, and incidental expense such as tips. The cost attributable to a member of the family's going along on such trips may not be deducted. Keep a detailed record of the expenses incurred, such as cost of railroad fares, hotel bills, and so forth. Entertainment expense incurred during such trips must be connected with the profession.

Utility expense. The full cost of heat, light and gas may be deducted, in so far as such items relate to business use.

Charitable contributions. Contributions made to charitable organizations for professional reasons may be deducted in full, without the normal 20 per cent of adjusted gross income limitation. A contribution made to a medical group of a community chest drive would be treated as a business charitable contribution. Although the value of time devoted to free clinics may not be deducted, the cost of transportation, including gasoline, in going to and from the clinic may.

Postgraduate education. The cost of acquiring a medical education at college or medical school may not be deducted, nor may the expense of taking board examinations. The cost of postgraduate courses to prepare for a specialty is not deductible either.

Recently, however, it was held that the expense incurred by a specialist in attending a course relating to his specialty could be deducted, since such attendance had a direct relation to the production of professional income by the specialist, and the expense was attributable to his need to keep abreast of new procedures.

Uniforms and laundry expense. The cost of office uniforms may be deducted, as well as laundry charges and repairs. One may also deduct such costs for linens and towels. If a rental service is employed, the full rental cost may be deducted.

Check List of Expense

The following check list of professional expense will be useful in keeping track of deductible items:

Accountants' fees relating to the practice

Attorneys' fees relating to the practice

Automobile expense, including maintenance, chauffeur's salary, insurance, depreciation, garage, rent, parking fees, tolls, license fees and plates

Board and lodging furnished an employee for the employer's convenience

Books, magazines, newspapers, flowers, cigarettes for the waiting room

Christmas presents or bonuses to employees

Cleaning woman's wages

Charitable contributions

Depreciation of office equipment, building, books

Electricity expense

Entertainment expense

Gifts to hospital attendants and nurses

Interest attributable to office

Insurance premiums

Medical and office supplies

Professional dues

Repairs to equipment and office

Rent, including any other charges paid

Salaries paid to nurse, assistant, domestics

Taxes, including those on sales, license fees, real property, gross receipts

Telephone and telegraph expense

Travel expense

Uniform and laundry expense

Since the tax law is subject to almost daily changes by reason of congressional legislation, court decisions and rulings of the Treasury Department, it would be well to consult your attorney or accountant on particular problems affecting your practice. In any event, he should be consulted on the tax consequences of receipt of other than professional income, or payment for other than professional expense, since the above discussion has not dealt with these matters.

18

Economic Security

by John Alan Appleman

THE NEED FOR SPECIALIZED ASSISTANCE

THE PROBLEM of economic security concerns the physician not only for himself but for those dependent upon him — his wife, his children, and occasionally his grandchildren, parents, and other relatives. With certain limitations, the analysis of these problems and lending of specialized assistance in their solution falls in the field of what is called estate analysis or estate planning. This requires a knowledge of rather intricate aspects of the law — primarily in the fields of insurance, probate, wills, trusts, taxation, and future interests. Unfortunately, specialists are as yet few in number, since the busy family attorney, enmeshed in a multitude of diverse phases of the law, does not have the time to concentrate in this field of activity (1). Furthermore, lawyers are not permitted to list their fields of special qualification. If the physician desires expert help, he must find his expert — making pertinent inquiries about training and background — and even substantial fees will thereby be saved, many times over, to the physician and to his estate. Above all, he must avoid reliance upon legal advice offered by laymen who may utilize some learned-sounding language or purport to render estate planning services, but may actually open up a thousand pitfalls for him.

A PROPER MENTAL APPROACH

When we speak of economic security, we must remember that security is, itself, a relative term. To one working as an intern, an earlier graduate's income of $10,000 a year generally seems quite large. Yet a physician with an income of $25,000 a year may not feel prosperous, any more than does the business leader in this income bracket. There are too many things competing for slices of his income. Similarly, it is impossible for the physician to give all members of his family perfect financial security either during his lifetime or upon his death. The man who seeks to do so and drives himself intolerably hard, becoming a tense and nervous husband or father — who breeds ulcers and hypertension in himself or others in order to accomplish such unattainable objectives — is unwise. Life is meant to be lived in the present tense, not in retrospect when the candle of life grows dim. Yet too few persons realize this factor and may sacrifice that which is worth while in life for a financial will-o'-the wisp (2).

This is the first thing for the physician to consider in undertaking to analyze his affairs and to chart a path either for his future career or for those years that may remain to a man already well advanced in his professional life. Personal factors may cause an economic shipwreck or keen distress to the individual. One of these factors is that, in these days, the physician's income frequently develops too rapidly. Having saved and labored for long years, when other people of comparable age were beginning to surround themselves with the luxuries of life, the physician and his wife often feel that they have to make up for lost time. This is a materialistic age and the urge is strong to want too much too fast.

In these days when high income taxes, grocery bills, utilities, and other current expenses leave a minimum of capital savings with which to pay for luxury items, it must be understood that these goals are not attainable in a single year or even in five years.

It is far better for the physician to persuade his wife to read
these pages, to discuss their problems frankly together, and to
face squarely their social and economic temptations, than to
plunge onto the never ending treadmill of keeping up with the
Joneses. Many a sound physician's tranquillity or health has been
broken from trying to meet this pace. All that is required to
combat this urge is patience, an ability to look at oneself honestly,
and a sense of humor. May I repeat that the first essential, then,
is "Physician, heal thyself" of untoward social ambition if a tran-
quil and happy life is desired?

WISDOM OF A CONSERVATIVE INVESTMENT PROGRAM

Economic security may usually be attained if one acquires, over
a period of years, equities of various types that enhance in
value. These may develop in part by methods that are not normally recognized as avenues of savings — such as payments on
a home or on life insurance premiums. If these averaged out,
over a thirty-year period, together with other savings or investments, at $5000 a year (and in peak years they might be con-
siderably greater) the total accumulation alone would amount
to $150,000. Interest earned and enhancing the total — even with-
out rising capital values — would bring it to an amount in excess
of $200,000. Therefore, it is clearly not necessary to plunge into
risky or untried ventures in an effort to achieve financial security
too rapidly. One is more apt to lose one's entire capital accumula-
tions by trying to compete in an unfamiliar field. Physicians are
notoriously easy marks for fast promoters of every type. Isn't it
time to reverse this tendency?

GENERAL PRINCIPLES OF INVESTMENT

If you want to invest, the best time to do it, as a rule, is when
others are following an opposite course. Most people sell stocks

or farms in the middle of a depression. That is of course the best time to buy — not on the boom markets, when the income, averaged over a twenty-year basis, will not return over 1 to 2 per cent annually upon the investment.

It is not possible to find an investment counsel in any area who is expert on all possible methods of investment. The stockbroker is no expert on farms or rental real estate. Each of these investment subjects could fill a text. Let me pass along just a few comments which may be of help.

Try to diversify your holdings to the extent that 25 per cent or better of net worth is in "equity holdings" — such as soundly chosen common stocks.

If you cannot afford a widely diversified stock portfolio, check over investment syndicate stocks or mutual funds shares offering this diversification. However, study their past records with care and bear in mind that an excellent record for the period from 1940 onward does not mean that a like result would follow if we encountered a new era similar to that from 1929 to 1938. Also, buy for the long pull, and preferably in the field of "growth" type securities. Don't purchase stock research services in an effort to try to become your own expert. Many brokers have read them for years and are far from financially secure.

If you buy farm land, buy it in your own county or near your home where you can talk to the tenant over the telephone, watch his performances, and replace him if necessary. Buy the best land, not the poorest, though it costs you more — but buy it in a period when the price is not three times its average cost over the past twenty years. And don't put the money back into farmhouses. Such items are nonproductive and expensive. Land with no buildings at all, rented out to an adjacent farmer, is usually the most satisfactory — unless you choose to live on the farm yourself.

If you buy rental real estate, don't buy the lovely and expensive properties — for example, a $30,000 property that brings in

$150 a month. Buy, instead, property that will gross between 15 and 25 per cent per year, and net not less than 10 per cent. It may not give you the pride of possession — but it's a far better type of investment. And commercial real estate, for many reasons, is generally better than residential real estate.

You should select investments that fit your personality. One person will gravitate naturally toward farms; another will shun rental real estate because he fears vacancies, plumbing bills, and similar problems; still another may have a phobia of the stock market. Each person should select the type of investment with which he will be content, but seek to diversify his holdings between dollar type and equity type of holdings so that he can face the hazards of inflation and deflation with equal equanimity. No estate analyst is going to give the physician investment advice in any specific detail, because of the wide variation in clients' personalities and variations in opportunities according to localities. Each man must work out for himself the basic approaches to investment that will suit him best and then obtain the advice of several competent and honest persons familiar with investments available within those narrow limits.

As a physician you should bear in mind even more keenly than a layman the possibility of "little strokes." These may affect your business acumen in later years and cause the dissipation of your funds. It would not be amiss, after the investment program is quite well crystallized — perhaps by age 50 — to shift the assets to a corporate trustee, with reasonable restrictions against your own improvidence, as much as can be done consistent with prevailing state law. And if you are fearful of your own judgment, or desirous of ridding yourself of investment problems, these duties can be shifted from their very inception to a corporate trustee. It should be understood, however, that such a trustee will generally be ultraconservative, which means that any enhancement thereafter in capital worth will be quite modest.

CREATING AN INSURANCE PROGRAM

To turn now from ways to enhance capital to ways to keep from losing it. Doubtless the quickest forms of loss are those occurring through casualties and catastrophes. In the former, we generally consider injuries to the person; in the latter, damage to personal or to real property.

No physician is so wealthy that he can afford to carry from his personal funds all of his risks of possible loss. Nor would he be wise to do so even if he could, since he is not an expert in the handling of claims and litigation. So he, and others like him, pool their resources together and hire experts to exercise such supervision. This we call insurance.

It is inadvisable for the physician to shop around personally for the numerous coverages that he will require. He is far too busy to be bothered with such details; in addition, his inexperience will generally produce an overlapping, expensive, and inadequate program. The best way to put such a plan into operation is to find a good reputable broker and have him handle all of these policies, other than life insurance, through major companies. Give such a broker your instructions, and if he neglects his duties, replace him. Having a single broker at any one time will also avoid the time wasted in listening to a dozen competing agents on each coverage.

It is recommended also that renewals be planned to fall due on a single, or perhaps semiannual, date — e.g., June 1, or perhaps May 1 and October 1 if two dates are desired, to make it easy to check your coverages, even though this produces a good-sized bill arriving upon one or two occasions. It is better not to have this bill fall due at the same time as that of substantial income or real estate tax payments. Life insurance should not be handled by this broker, nor would life insurance premiums necessarily bear the same anniversary date as the other coverages.

The following are some of the coverages necessary to be taken into consideration:

Liability Coverages

Malpractice. Any reputable insurer is satisfactory, but purchase the largest limits you can secure. Anyone can err, and today's juries place no lid on damage verdicts.

O., L. and T. The full name is owner's, landlord's and tenant's liability insurance. It protects you, whether you are the owner or the tenant, against suits by someone who has slipped in that pool of warm water the nurse spilled upon the floor and neglected to mop up, or has fallen on the too slick floor or the dimly lit stair. Carry at least $50,000/100,000/50,000. These terms, which I shall use also in subsequent discussion, mean simply this — $50,000 limit for bodily injuries to any one person arising from a single accident; $100,000 limit for all persons receiving bodily injuries in a single accident; $50,000 limit for all property damage caused in a single accident. Similar insurance should be carried upon all properties that you own other than your home, which is handled differently, as will be pointed out in the paragraph on comprehensive personal liability.

Workmen's compensation. This need be carried only when you operate a structure, when your employees handle certain types of tools, or under other circumstances required by state law. Give your attorney the full facts and secure a written opinion from him regarding the necessity or nonnecessity of such insurance in your case. In any event, you may need an employer's liability policy, or an endorsement to one of the other types of liability policies mentioned herein, to protect against civil liability to your employees arising other than under compensation statutes. Such other policies frequently exclude injuries to employees, so that this loophole must be plugged by proper insurance.

Comprehensive personal liability. This covers legal liability arising from home accidents and from personal acts of you and members of your family, such as slicing a golf ball or mistaking a farmer's cow for a deer. Carry at least 50,000/100,000/50,000 — as explained in the paragraph on owner's, landlord's and tenant's liability insurance.

Automobile liability. Carry the largest liability limits obtainable — at a very minimum, 100,000/250,000/50,000, and preferably even more than $50,000 for property damage. You could collide with a tank truck and burn up an entire suburb. Comprehensive, medical, and emergency road service are nice frills and comforting to have, but the lack of them would not produce bankruptcy in the event of loss. Similarly, a physician can afford to carry a $250 deductible or other low-cost collision coverage, instead of the more common and more expensive types. He can absorb the small property loss, if necessary, but he cannot act as banker against the heavy liability hazards.

Property Insurance Coverages

I recommend particularly the following types of policies:

Personal property floater coverage. This is the first of the non-liability coverages to be discussed. It can well be carried with a nonconference company at a deviated rate on a three- or five-year basis, preferably, again, with a $50 or $100 deductible provision. A conference company is one that adheres to a standard rate fixed by an actuarial bureau. A company not bound by such an arrangement is frequently called a "nonconference" company and often writes such insurance at a rate "deviated" from, or lower than, the standard rate — either by simply charging a smaller premium, or by returning a dividend of 15 to 25 per cent of the premium at the end of the policy term. Of course, the stability of such a company should be established.

A floater policy protects against loss of personal property (other than office property, unless this is added by endorsement) by fire, theft, disappearance, and other casualties at home or away from home. If office furniture and equipment are not added to this policy by endorsement, simple fire and extended coverage insurance on the office furnishings is generally adequate. I have never heard of a thief stealing an X-ray machine.

Fire and additional extended coverage. This should be carried on any real estate that the physician owns or that he has any interest in, generally again on a three- or five-year basis. Again, it can frequently be secured at a deviated rate, as explained above. Avoid, however, coinsurance, which may save premiums now but prove expensive in the event of loss. Coinsurance is insurance in which the company bears the entire risk up to the policy limit — *provided,* however, and this is important — that such insurance is in the full value, or proportion of value required, of the property insured. If such insurance is carried in the amount of only half the value, the company pays for only one-half the loss. In this day of rapidly mounting values, and particularly where reconstruction costs greatly exceed cash market values, coinsurance can easily lead to arguments, upon the occurrence of a loss.

Health and Accident Coverages

Now let us take a brief look at health and accident insurance. In life we have to take certain chances and to assume certain risks. A good place to do so is with this form of insurance, in order to save the otherwise necessary expenditure of premiums. As yet, disability insurance has not been designed for the needs of the professional man. So long as either an attorney or a physician can see people, or even converse with them, he is not totally and permanently disabled, though he be confined to a wheel chair or to his bed. He is far better off, as a rule, to save his premiums than to buy coverages that do not fit his needs (3).

The short-term loss the physician can absorb himself. The rare situation of an extended or even of true permanent disability he could not — but he must decide if the gamble is worth the premium. If he decides to insure, then to hold down expense he should purchase nothing other than lifetime protection against disability, defined in terms of his occupation and purchased on a noncancellable basis from a company of excellent repute, and accept a long waiting period — thirty, sixty, or even ninety days — after the origin of the accident or disease. Some group plans offer rather reasonable protection in a semi-noncancellable form, whereas other policies are subject to definite criticism. Since disability policies vary widely, even within a single company, each must be analyzed separately when presented. Normally, however, I prefer sound health and accident policies over disability riders added to life insurance contracts, even though the latter may provide for lifetime reimbursement in the event of total permanent disability.

Life Insurance

Life insurance is in quite a different category from health and accident coverages. Such insurance should be the first major purchase by a physician. It is the only means by which he can buy a ready-made estate on the installment plan, to protect his wife and children in the event of his premature death (4). This is no time, in his early years, for frills — such as educational policies for the children, retirement income insurance, or high-cost contracts. He should buy, as quickly as possible, $100,000 of convertible term insurance with a sound major company with which he will be willing to carry his insurance program the rest of his life — and let the dividends reduce the insurance cost. As soon as he can afford to do so, he should convert to ordinary life insurance — and, if his means are ample, let the dividends, if the policy is of a participating type, accrue to pay up the insurance more quickly. He has thus given his family immediate protection; he has guarded against the risk of later uninsurability; and later, as means permit, he will be able to embark upon a retirement program. As funds increase, the physician may also add additional contracts with still greater savings features. And, by all means, he should include waiver of premium provisions in the event disability should prevent his discharge of his premium obligations.

Let us explain, briefly, the chief terminology used in this field and then illustrate some of the representative types of policies. The two major kinds of life insurance evolve from the nature of the company issuing the policy. The majority of life insurance is issued by mutual companies. Those contracts are termed "participating" policies, which means, simply, that a portion of the premium is returned annually in the form of dividends. Such dividends can be used either to reduce the premium, to shorten the premium paying period, or to add to the policy protection.

Policies issued by stock companies are "nonparticipating," which means that they are figured on a net cost basis and return no dividends. The gross premiums quoted on such insurance are always lower; but the question of ultimate net cost depends on the particular company and its experience over a period of years.

The premium that the insured pays is divided into two parts: (1) the net premium, which is, in turn, subdivided into (a) the current year mortality element and (b) the current year increase to policy reserve; and (2) expense loading. It is obvious that the mortality element, or risk of death, increases each year. That is one reason why insurance costs less when taken at an earlier age. Not only is the mortality risk less, but the company has the use of the money longer to secure earnings and thus to increase the policy reserve. These earnings from the reserve are carefully computed with the mortality element in order to establish a "level premium," which is not subject to increase as the insured grows older.

Obviously, then, since the cost of the mortality feature will be the same at age 35, whether the insured carries term insurance,

TYPES OF INSURANCE CONTRACTS: COST, VALUES AT AGE 65, AND PROJECTED DIVIDENDS

(All figures are based on units of $1000 of life insurance.)

Age of Insured	Gross Premium, Participating	Average Projected Dividend 1st year to 20th	Premium, Nonparticipating	*W. P., Participating	*W. P., Nonparticipating	Guar. Cash Value Age 65, Participating	Projected Dividend Additions Age 65	Guar. Cash Value Age 65, Nonparticipating	Paid-up Insurance Age 65, Participating	Paid-up Insurance Purchased by Dividend Additions	Paid-up Insurance Age 65, Nonparticipating
**Ten-Year Convertible Term Insurance ** **											
25	$ 8.50	$3.18–4.26	$ 6.59	$ .32	$ .42						
30	9.98	3.72–5.08	7.01	.43	.52						
40	15.54	5.44–6.44	10.60	.94	1.00						
50	28.08	7.07–9.20	20.63	2.40	2.83						
Ordinary Life (Payments so long as one lives)											
25	20.60	3.66– 8.53	16.56	.45	.59	$628.11	$542.00	$ 597.00	$ 790.00	$ 682.00	$ 793.00
30	23.73	4.24– 9.49	19.10	.57	.73	660.35	469.00	566.00	755.00	590.00	755.00
40	32.55	6.15–12.10	26.67	.99	1.27	522.10	323.00	492.00	656.00	407.00	653.00
50	46.99	7.93–14.80	39.72	1.88	2.61	393.94	190.00	365.00	495.00	239.00	484.00
Twenty Pay Life (Payments for twenty years only)											
25	33.79	3.65–10.75	28.16	.32	.43	795.30	544.00	754.00	1000.00	684.00	1000.00
30	36.05	4.11–11.50	30.78	.41	.52	795.30	467.00	754.00	1000.00	587.00	1000.00
40	44.89	5.90–13.18	38.13	.85	1.06	795.30	327.00	754.00	1000.00	411.00	1000.00
50	56.69	7.96–14.62	49.57	1.94	2.70	586.81	194.00	550.00	1000.00	244.00	1000.00
Retirement Income Age 65 * (Matures as cash endowment)**											
25	34.43	3.67–11.09	30.79	.64	.79	1623.00	746.00	1664.00	1623.00	746.00	1664.00
30	41.07	4.30–12.48	36.77	.83	1.02	1623.00	640.00	1664.00	1623.00	640.00	1664.00
40	62.54	6.44–17.28	57.60	1.51	1.08	1623.00	448.00	1664.00	1623.00	448.00	1664.00
50	112.22	9.40–23.36	106.72	3.11	4.83	1623.00	274.00	1664.00	1623.00	274.00	1664.00

* W. P. = waiver of premium cost per $1000 of insurance.

** In some companies, the insured must convert within the eighth year under a ten-year convertible term policy.

*** $2500 paid each year commencing at age 35, with one company, would give an insurance feature of $75,000 if the insured died prematurely. At age 65 the total cash value, including dividends, would amount to $108,250 and provide a life income of $666.82 a month on a ten-year certain basis or $595.37 on an installment refund basis.

ordinary life insurance, or some form of endowment insurance, it is apparent that the amount of money left from the premium payment to accumulate at interest depends on the size of the premium paid. If the mortality element at age 35 is $10 per $1000 and the expense loading is $2, and the insured pays only $12, there is nothing left to go into the reserve. If he pays $25, there will be $13 left; if he pays $50, there will be $38. In each case, there is the same amount of life insurance protection *during the policy period;* the difference is in the amount of savings feature.

The different types of contracts, their cost as between an excellent mutual and an excellent stock company at present rates, guaranteed cash values at age 65, and projected dividends are illustrated in the table. It will readily be seen that the higher premium contracts accumulate greater cash values — but provide, proportionately, far less protection. At age 40, $2500 a year in premium payments will buy better than $90,000 of ordinary life insurance, whereas it will buy only $65,000 of twenty pay life — but the latter contract will, at the end of twenty years, have greater loan or cash surrender values. Therefore, for the young man, the goal normally should be large protection and small savings features; for the older man thinking of retirement, larger savings features and less protection.

Life insurance has its great values. They are too numerous to relate here. Its settlement options, for one thing, afford flexible media for providing fixed payments to one's widow or children without trustee's expenses. But life insurance has its limitations also. For a physician to embark upon a top-heavy program, neglecting all other forms of retirement accumulation — unless he is otherwise incapable of wise saving — is not to be advised. Nor, under today's rates, can annuities be recommended except in rare instances in which they may be purchased on the counsel of an estate analyst.

WILLS AND TRUSTS

The next major step to be considered in the field of estate planning is that of testamentary instruments — or the legal papers by which one provides for the care of his survivors. For the young physician this means two wills — one for himself, and one for his wife, with testamentary trust provisions in case both parents die while one or more children are minors.

I become properly irked when I hear of lawyers, in their blithe ignorance, addressing luncheon clubs about estate problems and exhorting the merits of a short, simple will. Such an instrument means simply that you have dumped your problems into the lap of the probate court — and that the judge, a stranger, must guess as to what your wishes were, since you failed to be explicit.

When the physician is first entering practice, this instrument (except where parental care is necessary) should usually leave everything to the wife, with only those strings that may be necessary for her protection. In the event of her death, a trustee should be designated to handle the property for the children until they come of age (5). Preferably this should be a substantial banking institution in the state where the children will be living. A guardian should be selected to rear those children who may then be minors, if both parents are deceased. The guardian should be, if possible, a relative whose age and tastes are similar to those of the parents. Arrangements should be made for the trustee to pay sufficient funds to the guardian for the maintenance and education of the children. Life insurance proceeds remaining after the widow's death would normally be added to the trust corpus for greater flexibility in total administration.

Such a will must provide for equalizing the shares of children fairly, since they will usually be of different ages when their parents die and will have received varying years of parental support. One must analyze the possible careers they may follow, and if a male child elects a long period of college training, the testator should treat a female child fairly who may marry at the age of 18 years. The parent must also distinguish between desirable security and destruction of incentive; between alleviation of hardship and creating an Old Man of the Sea which may destroy a daughter's marriage when her husband feels his family leadership has been undermined by her financial independence, or when she becomes more eager to walk out after a quarrel than to kiss and make up.

TAX SAVINGS FACTORS

When you have begun to accumulate a substantial estate, your emphasis may then — but not until then — shift toward tax savings. The principles of tax savings are basically simple, although the proper carrying out of such principles is enmeshed in difficulties. To save income taxes, income must be split between more low-base taxpayers. Since individually earned income cannot be so apportioned or split, except from the split-income provisions of the income tax law, gift or sale devices may be used to shift investment income to other members of a family, one or more corporations, or to one or more trustees (5). Thus, if Dad is in a 60 per cent income tax bracket, any rental income from investment property leaves him only 40 per cent. By conveying such property to his two sons, or to a trustee, with a presently low or nonexistent tax rate, the tax consequences may be cut by half or more, leaving larger net sums for family use. What may be entirely appropriate in one case may be completely inappropriate in another. The devices used must be carefully selected with expert help and skillfully drafted.

In addition to income tax savings, sound planning requires consideration of federal estate taxes, state inheritance taxes, administration expenses, and shrinkage that might result from forced liquidation of estate assets at figures below their values to pay claims and other charges. For estate tax purposes, all property in which the decedent had an interest at the time of his death is included — even joint tenancy property and life insurance which he has made expressly payable to his wife or children. The first $60,000 of such estate is exempt from federal taxes, the rate thereafter commencing at 3 per cent and rising to a top of 77 per cent. State inheritance taxes usually increase in proportion to the size of the bequest and the remoteness of kinship of the legatee. All of such items may bite off substantial chunks of a poorly planned estate.

One method of accomplishing savings in estate taxes is by the use of the marital deduction, or split-estate method, in the physician's will. He may leave up to one-half of his estate outright to his widow, free from estate tax, those assets then being subject to tax in her estate if they remain at that time. The other half he may leave to a trustee in such a way that his widow may receive the income of it, if that is what he wants to accomplish. That half only will be taxed in the physician's estate but it will escape taxation in his widow's estate. Various methods of using all or portions of the marital deduction will suggest themselves, depending upon the situation.

Another method whereby the physician may reduce potential estate taxes is giving away portions of the estate while he is living. By proper planning, he can give large portions to his children during his lifetime with no tax consequences — and, in any event, a gift tax will usually be far less than the comparable estate tax on the same property or money. There are several reasons for this. Each spouse has a $3000 annual exemption for each donee. In addition to these annual exemptions, each spouse has a $30,000 gross exemption which may be consumed before any gifts are subject to gift tax. Since both estate taxes and gift taxes are progressive, the making of a gift normally takes such property from the top of the applicable estate tax brackets and moves it down to the lowest gift tax brackets. The gift tax rate is only three-fourths of the estate tax rate upon property in the same tax bracket. The warning must be advanced, however, to make haste slowly and only with the most careful of expert guidance.

NATURE AND METHOD OF PRACTICE

The physician must also consider the method in which he is going to conduct his professional practice, whether it will be as an employee, either of a corporation, a clinic, or a partnership; as a sole practitioner; or as a partner in a clinic or other entity. Such a decision depends largely upon the individual himself — his type of practice, his personality, his energy, his gregariousness, and similar factors. No estate analyst is going to tell him to throw up his job and seek another. Estate planning is undertaken by lawyers specializing in specific phases of the law — not by psychoanalysts or employment counselors. One would be presumptuous in attempting to advise the very individual who knows more about himself and his adaptability to these factors than does any third person.

However, a few recommendations must be made. The first is that any lasting relation must be built upon solid rock. It must be established between individuals who both respect and like each other thoroughly, who are equally energetic and willing to assume responsibility, and whose integrity is above reproach. It would be better if they lived in different parts of the town and did not visit back and forth socially. Even in large clinics, intra-clinic social affairs seldom work out happily.

A clinic must have a sound program for pensions and advancement if it expects to retain qualified personnel upon a nonpartner basis. In this regard, I strongly counsel against the use of an "association" or the like at the present time. The experiments in this direction are still fraught with danger of an explosive quality — such as taxation of all funds used for distribution, other than as salary payments, to the members upon a regular corporation tax rate plus possible 75 or 85 per cent surtax penalties as a personal holding company. There are enough safe and orthodox methods so that dangerous experimentation can well be left to the more venturesome person who is willing to pay heavy penalties if he guesses wrong.

A partnership should be spelled out in writing with sufficient detail to clarify any reasonably probable contingencies. A sound "buy and sell" agreement (6), arranging for the payment of a retiring or deceased partner's interest by the continuing partner or partners, particularly if funded by life insurance, has its place in such a procedure. These matters can be worked out by an expert when the details and problems are known.

NECESSITY OF REGULAR AUDITS

There is a final suggestion that may be helpful to physicians. It is suggested that each practitioner or partnership engage a certified public accountant on an annual basis to make a monthly audit and an annual report, as well as to prepare the tax returns. He will not only detect, as a rule, employee pilfering or waste in early stages, but will correct habits of permitting large receivables to accumulate, and keep the physician out of difficulty with Uncle Sam. But the physician must remember that the accountant is not an estate analyst and is no more qualified in matters of estate planning than is a life underwriter. Each man has a value within his field, but not beyond it.

SUMMARY

Estate planning, and planning for economic security, it will be seen, therefore, are lifetime projects — not one-shot affairs. The expert can start the physician on a proper path, or redirect his steps if they have strayed. From time to time he can help the

physician to check his bearings. But it is for the physician himself to set his goal and to strive for its fulfillment. In this, however, he must be certain that he does not substitute false idols for
those that are worthy of him. The companionship of one's wife,
the laughter of one's children, are of far greater value than mere
monetary accomplishments. The respect of one's colleagues and
of the community are precious things. Happiness cannot be
bought with money, but only with an appreciation of life and
the living of a philosophy that is true to one's own character.
Those objectives the physician should reanalyze as frequently as
he does his plans for financial success and economic security.

REFERENCES

1. APPLEMAN, JOHN ALAN. Estate Analysis: The Role of the Family
   Attorney. *American Bar Association Journal,* December, 1950.
2. APPLEMAN, JOHN ALAN. Even Physicians Die. *Journal of the American Medical Association,* December 15, 1951; A Chart for Living. *Quarterly of Phi Beta Pi,* March, 1952. A Specialist Looks
   at Your Tax Problems. *Bulletin of Los Angeles County Medical Association,* November 6, 1952; Now Is the Time. *The
   Rotarian,* May, 1953.
3. APPLEMAN, JOHN ALAN. Jokers Cost Money. *Mississippi Law Journal,* December, 1951, reprinted in *Federation of Insurance
   Counsel Quarterly,* July, 1952; Health and Accident Insurance
   Policies. *Reader's Digest,* September, 1953; A & H Insurance Needs Improvement. *The Spectator,* November, 1953.
4. APPLEMAN, JOHN ALAN. The Underwriter's Role in Estate Analysis. *The Insurance Salesman,* May, June, July, August, and
   September, 1953; and the monthly series in *The Spectator* com-
   mencing in February, 1954.
5. APPLEMAN, JOHN ALAN. Estate Planning: A Practical Approach.
   Taxes, August, 1953.
6. APPLEMAN, JOHN ALAN. A New Approach to Buy and Sell Agreements. *Taxes,* October, 1952.

19

Medicine and the Law

by Louis J. Regan

LEGAL MEDICINE is frequently defined as the application of medical knowledge to the needs of justice. However, a more precise view of the subject can be achieved by separating it into two major divisions. The first involves the physician's practice of his special skills in medicolegal investigations: the second involves a legal evaluation of his personal, ethical, and professional conduct.

MEDICOLEGAL INVESTIGATIONS

In situations in the first subdivision, the physician acts purely objectively, applying particular skills to the study of submitted matter and reporting on it or testifying to it. Such situations include the practice of forensic pathology, toxicology, hematology, and similar specialties.

The importance of improving medicolegal investigation becomes apparent when it is realized that about 20 per cent of all deaths in the United States result from violence or occur unexpectedly from obscure causes; that each year approximately one murder for every 10,000 living persons is officially recognized; and that since in many localities the investigation of violent or obscure deaths is insufficient, the number of murders that actually take place, or the number of deaths due to accident, suicide, or natural causes that are erroneously attributed to murder, cannot be estimated. Once these facts are understood, the vital need for more and better-qualified medicolegal investigators becomes apparent.

LEGAL ASPECTS OF MEDICAL PRACTICE

The more important phase of legal medicine is, however, the second subdivision — the phase in which a physician is personally involved in a case either as an expert witness or, through an allegation that he has infringed the law in some respect and has thus become subject to criminal or civil action or to citation before a board of medical examiners, as a defendant. For if a patient sues the physician and proves by a preponderance of all of the evidence that he suffered injury because the physician failed to act in accordance with the standard of practice in the community, the patient may recover a judgment for money damages. It is in this area that members of the medical profession need a more comprehensive educational program (1). This chapter can, of course, do no more than indicate the most essential areas in which the physician must be informed.

If a physician is to escape legal liability and penalty, it is obviously essential that he have some understanding not only of his legal obligation to his patient, but also of statutes and court decisions that apply to the physician-patient relation. The latter point is most obvious in cases concerning such matters as adoption, abortion, artificial insemination, sterilization, workmen's compensation, and narcotics.

In most jurisdictions the newly licensed physician must present his license for registration with the county clerk and, usually, with the local representative of the health department. Further, before he may dispense or prescribe narcotics, he must register with the Bureau of Narcotics of the Internal Revenue Service. In many jurisdictions it is required that a special prescription pad, obtainable from the state narcotic agency, be used in writing prescriptions for narcotic drugs. A copy of the state narcotic act may be obtained from the state narcotic agency. Information concerning federal narcotic regulations may be obtained from the local district supervisor, United States Bureau of Narcotics.

The state or local health department supplies various forms, together with essential pertinent information, that will permit the physician to know and comply with the law respecting the reporting of births, deaths, communicable diseases, and so on. In many states the law requires the physician to report to the chief of police (or to the sheriff) instances of violent or criminal injury. Such reports are not generally required for accidental injury unless the patient dies.

In all jurisdictions registration statutes require that a report of the birth, stillbirth, or death of an infant be filed with a designated agency. In such statutes a live birth is generally defined as one in which the child shows evidence of life after it is completely outside of the mother. Stillbirth refers to a fetus that shows no evidence of life after complete birth, providing uterogestation has advanced through 20 weeks, 5 months, or more.

In the event of a live birth followed by death, the filing of both a birth and a death certificate is necessary. In the case of stillbirth, the filing of a special stillbirth certificate is required in many states (Alabama, California, Connecticut, Florida, Idaho, Illinois, Indiana, Iowa, Louisiana, Maryland, Nevada, Ohio, Oregon, South Carolina, Utah, Virginia, Wisconsin, and Wyoming). Under statutes of other states, a stillbirth requires the filing of both a birth and a death certificate (Arizona, Colorado, Delaware, Georgia, Kentucky, Michigan, Missouri, Nebraska, New Jersey, New York, North Dakota, Pennsylvania, Rhode Island, Texas, Vermont, Washington, and West Virginia).

It is particularly to be borne in mind that each state has its own statutes forbidding an attending physician to sign a death certificate in certain cases. These cases generally include: any

violent or suspect death, whether homicidal, suicidal, or accidental; any death in which the physician has not been in attendance; any death in which the physician is unable to establish
the cause of death with reasonable clinical probability; any death
in which it appears that a criminal act may have been a con-
tributing cause. All cases coming within the provisions of the
statute must be referred to the designated authority, usually the
coroner or the medical examiner.

The physician entering practice needs to inform himself of the
provisions of the workmen's compensation act in his state. These
differ so much in detail in the several jurisdictions that generali-
zation concerning them is not profitable.

It may be generally stated that a physician is not likely to practice long in a given locality before it becomes necessary for him
to appear in court as an expert witness. Expert witnesses are
those who are skilled in any science, art, trade, or occupation. The
ordinary witness must, with few exceptions, testify to facts
within his own knowledge. In contradistinction, the expert witness is called upon to give opinion evidence. The medical expert
witness is used in a great variety of cases, such as criminal trials,
insanity and probate contests, cases arising under life, health,
and accident policies, and in personal injury actions.

It is probable that juries are more prone to distrust the testimony of the medical expert than that of any other witness.
(When a physician, in court or before the industrial accident
commission, presents himself successively as an expert in eight
or ten fields of specialty practice, it is not unreasonable to doubt
his qualifications or his integrity.) This being true, the content
of a medical expert witness's opinion may be only a little more
important than the manner in which he delivers it — than the
impression he makes on the jury.

The expert should be professional in manner, using language
understandable to the lay jury. He should be earnest and sincere,
and avoid the appearance of being an advocate for any party. It

is his function and privilege to contribute to the end that truth and justice may prevail.

No reasonable person will argue with the theory of law providing that a person who has been injured by the carelessness or ignorance of another person should be compensated for that injury; the fact that the injury has been caused by a physician affords no ground for varying from the rule.

There are meritorious malpractice claims — cases in which patients suffer injury as a result of the ignorance or negligence of physicians. The honest physician need have no fear of such a suit. He can avoid being justly charged with malpractice by caring for every patient with scrupulous attention to the requirements of good practice. On the other hand, the majority of all malpractice claims and suits that are brought against physicians are nonmeritorious; that is, they are not justly founded. Such claims are injurious to the profession and to the public alike.

Any patient may bring a malpractice action against any physician who has attended him professionally, although the Statute of Limitations provides a time after which specified actions are barred. The bringing of such an action does not, of course, suggest that the claim has any merit. Nevertheless, the practitioner who is the target of the accusation is damaged by the mere filing of the action.

When a patient alleges that he has suffered an injury because his medical attendant failed to care for him in accordance with the standards of skill, care, judgment, and diligence that are commonly possessed and exercised by reputable practitioners in the community, the physician is being accused of professional negligence. He is charged with malpractice.

In other words, professional negligence or malpractice consists in a physician's doing something he should not do or failing to do something that he should do in the professional care of a patient. The criterion for evaluating a physician's handling of a case is what the average physician in the community. in the same field of practice, would or would not do in similar circumstances.

If physicians were always able to obtain perfect results there would, of course, be no malpractice actions. But deaths, untoward and unexpected results, continuing disabilities and complications occur and will continue to occur. Whether or not the patient brings an action is often determined by his feeling toward his physician. A patient who has a friendly feeling for the physician and who believes that everything possible has been done for him is not likely to sue for malpractice, even when the result is bad. Such suits are likely if the patient is resentful of some fancied or actual affront, if he believes that he has not been closely enough attended, or, above all, if a third person raises a doubt in his mind regarding the propriety of the treatment.

A physician is not required to undertake the care of any patient; but once he assumes the responsibility he must give, or see to it that there is given, such care and treatment as the condition of the patient makes necessary until the patient no longer needs attention, unless the physician is sooner discharged or unless he withdraws from the case. Before a physician may withdraw from a case without legal liability, he must give reasonable notice of his intention and allow the patient reasonable opportunity to fill his place.

Many malpractice actions are brought as the result of some unwise statement made by the attending physician, or his partner, assistant, or office nurse, to the patient or to a friend of the patient. Care should be taken to avoid making any remark constituting an admission of fault or one that may be construed as such. An admission on the part of the defendant may free the plaintiff from the necessity of offering medical expert testimony; in the ordinary malpractice action, the alleged negligence of the defendant physician must be proved by medical expert testimony.

The application of the doctrine of *res ipsa loquitur* in a case gives rise to an inference of negligence on the part of the de-

fendant and relieves the plaintiff of the necessity of proving the
alleged malpractice by the testimony of experts; it places on the
defendant the burden of making explanation, if he can, to offset
the inference of negligence. *Res ipsa loquitur* (literally, the thing
speaks for itself) is a doctrine of the general law of negligence.
It is held applicable whenever one person is injured by an in-
strumentality entirely in the control of another person, the use
of which does not ordinarily result in injury if the person in
control exercises due care.

The doctrine of *res ipsa loquitur* has been held applicable in
the field of malpractice chiefly in cases that involve the slipping
of instruments, foreign bodies left in the tissues, burns from
heating modalities, roentgen radiation injuries (generally limited
to cases wherein the roentgen ray is being used diagnostically),
infection through the use of an unsterilized needle or instrument,
and injury to a portion of an anesthetized patient's body outside the field of treatment or operation.

The precipitating cause of many malpractice actions is found
in the unwise comments or criticism of physicians in regard to
treatment given to patients by other physicians. Commonly it is
criticism by a succeeding physician of the work of his predecessor
on the case. Various authorities have estimated that 50 to 80
per cent of all the suits for malpractice would be eliminated if
such destructive criticism could be stopped. It is profitless to attempt to determine why physicians are so prone to criticize
destructively and unethically, but the results of it are deplorable.
Legitimate criticism can rest only on full knowledge of the
facts as gathered from both sides — from the physician who
treated the patient as well as from the patient.

In the absence of evidence to the contrary, it is legally pre-
sumed that a physician exercises the ordinary skill and care required of him in treating his patient. He is justified in his conduct of the case if it is such as would be approved by even a
respectable minority of his associates in the same locality. A

charge of malpractice is not warranted even by the fact that he made a mistake in diagnosis or was guilty of an error of judgment, that he might have employed other medicines or used other methods of treatment, that expert witnesses testify that they themselves would have employed a different method, or that a bad result followed instead of a satisfactory one.

Experience has taught that the most careful attention to the dictates of good medical practice is not sufficient to ward off the unjust claim and that no physician is immune. The likelihood of being sued for malpractice must now be regarded as a definite occupational hazard for the practicing physician. *Caveat medicus!*

The physician-patient relationship is one of trust and confidence. The physician is obligated to act at all times with the utmost good faith toward his patient. Thus, if he knows that he cannot accomplish a cure or that the treatment adopted will probably be of no benefit, it is his duty to advise his patient of the facts. It is extremely doubtful that a physician has a therapeutic privilege to withhold a specific diagnosis from a patient sick with serious or fatal illness. On the contrary, it appears to be clear that, in ordinary circumstances, the confidential relationship requires that the physician make a frank and full disclosure when his patient is adult and mentally competent.

At common law, confidential communications made by a patient to a physician were not privileged. In some 31 American jurisdictions, this situation has been changed by statute. In 22 states, secrecy is required of the physician in criminal as well as in civil cases. The patient may waive the privilege by bringing certain actions as provided in the statutes, by implication through certain conduct on his part, or by direct and specific waiver. Most of the statutes on privileged communication cover judicial proceedings only; the privilege of silence applies only to matters that are essential to treatment or to medical consultation.

In any event, it is true, of course, that the *Principles of Ethics of the American Medical Association* require that confidences entrusted by the patient ordinarily must not be revealed and that the law of the right of privacy gives the patient additional protection. This is the right to be "left alone," or to live in seclusion without being subjected to unwarranted or undesired publicity. There should be no publication of a medical case record and no showing of a picture, still or motion, from which the identity of a patient is determinable, without the knowledge and authorization of the patient.

It is the personal concern of a physician for his patient that makes him different from a tradesman or a pure scientist. The secret of the care of the patient is in caring for the patient. The art of the practice of medicine is of extreme importance to the patient, and its good exercise is protective to the physician.

A good physician-patient relation depends not only on giving the best possible medical service, but also on maintaining the patient's confidence and friendship. Skill is no substitute for warmth or kindness. However, a physician is unwise who tells his patient "not to worry about a thing." Physicians should not guarantee results of treatments; malpractice actions arise if failure occurs (2).

The foregoing has touched upon the major areas of legal medicine. To this discussion should be added at least a few of the more important elements of prophylaxis against malpractice suits.

PREVENTION OF SUITS FOR MALPRACTICE

It is fundamental that every patient must be cared for with close attention to the requirements of good medical practice. This comprehends sufficiency of investigation, observation and treatment; and the utilization of every indicated laboratory aid. Thus, as stated in one legal case record, "The failure to make use of X-ray as an aid to diagnosis in cases of fracture amounts to a failure to use that degree of care and diligence ordinarily used by physicians of good standing in the community and the court, in absence of expert testimony, may take judicial notice of such fact." It includes the protection of those coming in contact with the patient; the instruction of the patient and of those caring for him so that all things needed may be carried out during the absence of the attending physician; and the recognition of the importance of psychologic factors so that the nervous, mental, and emotional balance of the patient may be constructively influenced by tactful handling and the institution of proper psychotherapeutic measures.

It is fundamental that, in undertaking the care of patients, the physician should accept only such cases as he is reasonably well qualified to handle. He must keep abreast of progress in his field of practice and should utilize only recognized and accepted procedures. In any case in which the patient is not doing well, in which there is any unexpected reaction or untoward occurrence, or in which he or his family complains or expresses dissatisfaction unduly, a consultant should be brought in. The consultation affords great protection in the event that a claim of malpractice is later made. It is recommended that protective use of consultants be made routine, even in cases in which fees for consultation may not be available.

It is important to exercise care in delegating duties to assistants, nurses, and technicians; in keeping up professional instruments and apparatus; and in maintaining a safe environment in which to work. Instruments should be checked and apparatus calibrated as required in the exercise of ordinary care.

It must be recognized that it is hazardous to sterilize any patient in the absence of a medical indication; that it is dangerous to telephone a prescription, because of the possibility of error in transmission; and that it is unwise for a physician to testify, without taking legal advice, at a coroner's inquest in a case in which he has been in professional attendance.

In any consideration precautions against claims of malpractice, the keeping of good medical case records must be emphasized.

It is desirable that a physician from time to time ask himself what he would wish to have in the record in the case under treatment in the event that he should later be called upon to justify in court his conduct of the case. "Ideal" medical records should be kept in every case: records that are presentable when offered in court; records that clearly show what was done and when it was done; records that indicate that nothing was neglected, that the care given fully met the standard demand by law. If a patient discontinues treatment before he should or fails to follow instructions, let the record show it. A good method is to file a carbon copy of the letter sent to the patient advising him against the unwise course. Although there is a legal presumption that a letter that has been mailed has been received by the addressee, there is no presumption that a letter has been mailed. The record should, of course, also contain the laboratory reports, consultants' reports, and certain miscellaneous forms that are necessary or desirable in particular cases, such as consent for operation, consent for autopsy, copies of reports required by law to be made, and acknowledgement of hazards of particular procedures (shock therapy, fever therapy, X-ray therapy).

Consent for operation must always be obtained. Any adult in a clear state of mind may authorize operation on himself. Oral consent might be considered sufficient, but because of the difficulty in proving that it was given, the physician should invariably require a witnessed consent in writing. If the patient is a minor (that is, a person under the age of 21), then consent is generally to be obtained from parent or guardian. If the patient is mentally incompetent, the consent of the one who stands in the position of guardian is required.

When an operation (such as vaccination, or sterilization under eugenic sterilization statutes) is made compulsory by law, the law furnishes the consent.

If an operation is unlawful, consent to its performance does not absolve the surgeon from liability. For example, all state statutes define the crime of abortion. In many the provision is that any abortion save one necessary to preserve the life of the woman is a crime; in some, the wording is, "necessary to save the life of the woman"; in 7 the statute reads, "preserve her life or that of her child." In 6 states this additional clause is found, "or abortion advised by two physicians to be necessary for that purpose." Four other states make the same provision with the advice of only one physician necessary. Abortion laws are highly varied. At the extreme, the statute of one state provides that *any* abortion is a crime.

A physician is well advised to be cautious and not to perform an abortion without first calling in reputable consultants and obtaining a concurrence of medical opinion on the necessity. An excellent practice now common in major hospitals is that of re-quiring the approval of a special committee of the staff before therapeutic abortion can be carried out in the institution.

In an emergency that demands immediate action for the pres-ervation of the life or health of a patient and in which it is not practicable to obtain his consent or the consent of anyone author-ized to speak for him, it is the duty of the attending physician to perform without consent such operation as good surgical practice demands.

If sterility is likely to result from surgery that is contemplated, explanation of that probability should be made and a signed au-thorization should generally be obtained from both spouses. On the other hand, there should be no promise or guarantee that the patient will be sterilized as the result of the procedure under-taken.

The individual physician must obtain consent to perform a post-mortem examination. This consent, too, should be in writ-ing and sufficiently comprehensive to allow the removal and taking away of tissue if such is to be done. In several states it is criminally illegal for any person to perform an autopsy with-out having first obtained the written authorization of the coroner or other authorized public officer, or of the person who has the right of disposition of the body.

If a physician attempts to justify his failure to continue in attendance on a patient under the claim either that the patient discharged him or that he withdrew from the case, the burden of proving the statement, so the courts have held, will be upon him. Therefore if he is discharged by a patient or if he withdraws from a case, a physician should invariably confirm the event in writing and file a carbon copy with the case record.

An examination of malpractice suits reveals the significant fact that malpractice claims arise almost invariably out of the first course of treatment. In other words, it is rare indeed that an old patient, unless justified, instigates a suit against his physician. It follows that the physician should be especially "malpractice-conscious" in dealing with the new or casual patient.

In conclusion, it is emphasized that the vast majority of malpractice actions can be avoided by scrupulous attention to the requirements of good medical practice; and that there will be few instances of injury resulting from the actions of misguided or malicious patients when practitioners understand fully how to protect themselves under the law. Prevention is the best defense against suits for malpractice.

REFERENCES

1. REGAN, L. J. *Doctor and Patient and the Law.* St. Louis: Mosby, 1949.
2. *Rx P.R.: A Public Relations Manual.* Chicago: American Medical Association, 1953.

INDEX

Index

ABORTIONS, 256
Abstract file, 135
Academic opportunities, in medical schools, 48–49
Accident insurance, 234
Account record, 195–196, 198
Accounting fees, 222
Administrative details, 116–117
Advisory Board of Medical Specialties, 70, 87–88, 106, 107
Aides. *See* Assistants, medical or office
Allergy, 45
Alpha Omega Alpha, 9
American Association of Medical Clinics, 77, 79, 87–88
American College of Physicians, 166
American Hospital Association, 106
American Journal of Clinical Pathology, 153
American Journal of Medical Technology, 153
American Medical Association: 111–115; woman's auxiliary, 27; on specialization, 69; House of Delegates, 70, 111–112; Council on Medical Education and Hospitals, 87, 106; Coun-

cil on Medical Service, 87, 186; group practice study, 87–88; journal, 106, 112, 113, 115, 132, 165; and specialty boards, 106–108; services, 113–115; councils and bureaus, 111–112; annual convention display of supplies, 158; principles of ethics, 184, 252
Anatomical Disquisition on the Motion of the Heart and Blood in Animals, An, 4
Anatomy, 47
Anatomy of Melancholy, The, 40
Anesthesiology, 74
Anesthesiology, American Board of, 107
Appointment book, 191
Appointment cards, 191–192
Appointment system, 187–190
Armed Forces Medical Library, *Current List of Medical Literature,* 136
Assistants, medical or office: and doctor's wife, 29; *1952* survey on, 177–178, 181; types, 178–179; selection and training, 179–180; wages, 181; functions and responsibilities, 188–189

Association of American Medical Colleges: 106; estimate of medical education costs, 167

Atchley, Dana W., "The Healer and the Scientist," 7

Audits, necessity of, 243

Auscultation, 4

Automobile: selection and care of, 175–176; liability insurance, 233

BACTERIOLOGY, 5

Bag, doctor's, equipment and drugs for, 160–162

Barbiturates, 163

Beckman, Harry (editor, *Year Book of Drug Therapy*), 166

Bethesda, Md., federal research hospital at, 49

Bigelow, Jacob, 11

Bills: discussing, 199; submitting, 200–202; collecting, 202–204

Biochemistry, 5, 47

Birth registrations, 247

Blue Shield, 67, 116

Bookkeeping, 206

Books, reference, 132

Books of account, 205–225

British Medical Journal, 91

British National Health Service, 91

Burton, Robert, 40

Business problems: of a beginning practitioner, 167–176; office records, 191–204; accounting and income tax, 205–225; economic security, 226–244

Business tax expense, 219

CABINET, for doctor's office, 158–159

Cabot, Richard, 137

Cardiology, 45

Cash disbursement book, 210, 214

Cash receipts books, 209–210

Charges, record of, 207–208

Charitable contributions, 224

Children, physician and his, 15–19, 32–34

Civic affairs, activity in, 17–18

Clinical Center, U.S. Public Health Service, 49

Clinical investigators, 48–49

Clinical research, opportunities in, 48–49, 102

Clinical specialties, 43, 45

"Clinicopathological" concept, 4

Clinics: group practice, 81, 82–88, 154; outpatient, 98–99, 102

Cohnheim, Julius Friedrich, 4

Collection agencies, 204

Collections, records of, 207–208

Community: physician in, 19–24; doctor's wife in, 26–27

Community medical resources: institutional and public agencies, 118–121; consultants, 121–122; government agencies, 123; voluntary agencies of health, 123; industrial medical departments, 123–124; public health agencies, 124–126; laboratory facilities, 151–152

Compulsory insurance, 99

Consultation room, 169

County medical society, 109–110, 185–186

Coverages, insurance, 232–238

Credit vs. cash purchasing, of equipment, 175

Cultural activities, 22

Current List of Medical Literature, 136

Cushing, Harvey, 132

DAY BOOK, 192–194
Death certificates, 247–248
Deductions, income tax, 217–225
Depreciable assets, 214
Depreciation, 219–221
Dermatology, 45
Dermatology and Syphilology, American Board of, 70, 107
Diagnosis, generalist's responsibility in, 62
Directory of Medical Specialists, 71
Directory of Medical Specialties, 70
Directory of State and Territory Health Authorities, 152
Disbursement book, cash, 210, 214
Disease, knowledge of causes, 4–5
District medical society, 21
Doctor. *See* Generalist, Physician, Specialist *and* Surgeon
Drug addicts, prescription regulations, 162–163
Drug therapy, 163–166
Drugs: needed by general practitioner, 157; for doctor's office, 159, 160; prescription and pharmacy relations, 159–160; in doctor's bag, 160–162; prescription regulations, 162–163
Dues, professional, 222

EDUCATION: of the generalist, 63–66; study, contacts, experience, 103–104; cost of physician's,

167; postgraduate, 224
Emergency calls, 160–162, 183–186
Endocrinology, 45
Entertainment expense, 223
Epitome of the Pharmacopoeia and National Formulary, 166
Equipment: laboratory, 142; for doctor's bag, 145–146, 160–162; importance of, 157; for doctor's office, 158–160, 168–172; purchasing of, 173–175
Estate tax savings devices, 241–242
Ethical Basis of Medical Practice, The, 10
Evening office hours, 190
Examination and treatment rooms, 169–172
Examining table, 158
Expenses, professional, deductions for, 217–225

FAMILY: physician and his, 14–19; medical attention for, 30–31; physician's responsibility to, 32–34
Family physician, 51. *See also* Generalist
Federal health agencies: Public Health Service, 126; Veterans' Administration, 126–128
Federal narcotics regulations, 162–163
Federation of State Medical Boards, 106
Fee splitting, 75–76
Filing and indexing, of reference material, 133–134

Filing system, for office records, 198

Financial problems: family, 35, 36; doctor's laboratory, 155; of beginning practitioner, 167–176

Fire insurance, 234

Floater insurance, 233–234

Food and Drug Administration: safeguards on new drugs, 164; surveillance of U.S.P. drugs, 166

Food and Nutrition, Council on (A.M.A.), 112

Freud, Sigmund, 40

Functional conditions, and generalist, 62

GASTROENTEROLOGY, 45

General medicine: 51–66; specialties vs., 71–72; basis of medical care, 107. *See under* Generalist

General Practice, American Academy of, 108–109, 166

General practitioner, 39, 51. *See also* Generalist

General surgeon, 69

Generalist: 39; function, 42, 62–63; vs. specialist, 46–47, 71–72; classes and patterns, 53–59; definition, 59–63; education, 63; hospital training, 63–64; advantages, 65; location, 66

Generalist-specialist, 53, 54, 55, 57, 58

Generalist-surgeon, 64

Geriatrics, 43

Gift tax savings, 241–242

Goldstein, M., 79

Governing boards, hospital, 90–91

Government agencies, 20, 123

Government research programs, 49

Group practice: benefits, 46–47; for generalists, 64; defined, 77; classifications, 78; development and growth, 78; advantages, 79–81; clinics, 81, 82–88, 154; future possibilities, 86–88

Guide to Services, index of services of A.M.A., 114

Gynecologist, 69

Gynecology, 45

HARRISON NARCOTIC ACT, 163

Harvey, William, 4

Health insurance: hospital plans, 93; medical plans, 93; compulsory, 99; advice on, 234

Health Education, Bureau of (A.M.A.), 112

Health Resources Advisory Committee, 14

Hippocratic era, 3

Hippocratic Oath, 9–10, 41

Home care, 94–95

Hospital care, 94–95

Hospital insurance, 93

"Hospital services," in generalist's training, 64

Hospital staff, physician's activities on, 21

Hospital training, for generalist, 63–64

Hospitals: functions, 89–90; governing boards, 90–91; doctor's affiliation with, 92–93; insur-

ance plans, 93; private patients' care, 93–94; value of good records, 97; doctor's duty to, 98–99; education of doctors in, 99–101; research opportunities in, 101–102
House of Delegates (A.M.A.), 111–112
Household help, 36
Hunt, G. H., 79

IDEALISM, in medicine, 72
Immunology, training in, 47
Income: specialist vs. general practitioner, 72; group practice clinics, 82–85
Income tax: bookkeeping records for, 205–215; deductions, 215–225; savings devices, 240
Index Catalogue of the Surgeon General's Library, 136
Industrial Health, Council on (A.M.A.), 112
Industries, medical departments, 123, 124
Instruments: laboratory, 114–145; office, 170–172
Insurance. *See under type of insurance*
Insurance broker, 231
Insurance coverages, for the physician, 232–238
Insurance expense, deductions for, 222
Interest expense, deductions for, 218–219
Internal medicine, 64
Internal Medicine, Board of: generalist's qualification require-

ments, 55; specialist's requirements, 69; substitute provisions made by, 107
Internist: term defined, 44; function of, 44–45
Internship: rotating type, 40, 63, 64; for generalist, 63–64
Investigations, medicolegal, 245–246
Investment, principles of, 228–230
It's Your A.M.A., index to services of A.M.A., 114

JOHNSON, SAMUEL, 41
Journal clubs, 104–105
Journal of the American Medical Association: specialty board requirements listed, 106; promotes basic policy of A.M.A., 112, 113; special issues, 115; required periodical, 132; information on new drugs, 164
Journal of Clinical Investigation, 153
Journal of Laboratory and Clinical Medicine, 153

LABORATORY: physical layout, 140; work space, 140–141; facilities, 141; equipment, 142; reagents, 143; instruments, 144–145; equipment for doctor's bag, 145–146, 161–162; maintenance, 142; repertoire, 146; laboratory tests, 148; technics, 150–151; community facilities, 151–152; personnel, 152–154; patient acceptance, 154–155; financing and administration, 155

Laennec, René T. H., 4
Lancet, 91
Laundry expense, 224
Legal fees, deductions for, 222
Legal medicine, 245–257
Legal Medicine, Bureau of (A.M.A.), 112
Legislation, Committee on (A.M.A), 112–113
Leisure time, 34
Liability insurance, 232–233
Library: physician's, 131–133; hospital or medical, 135–136
Life insurance, 235–238
Literature. *See* Medical literature

MacKenzie, Sir James, 4, 102
Malpractice: liability insurance, 232; claims against physician, 249–253; precautions against suits, 253–257
Marriage, as wife's career, 25
Massachusetts Medical Society, 11
Massage table, 158
Medical coverage; 183–186; weekend and night, 184–185
Medical Economic Research, Bureau of (A.M.A.), 112
Medical Economics, 177–178, 181
Medical Education and Hospitals, Council on (A.M.A.), 69–70, 87–88, 106, 111
Medical insurance, 93
Medical literature, 104–105, 134–135
Medical profession, choice of specialization, 39, 40, 41
Medical research, opportunities in, 48–49

Medical schools, academic positions in, 48–49
Medical Service, Council on (A.M.A.), 87–88, 111
Medical societies: district, 21; county, 109–110, 185–186; state, 110–111
Medical statesman, 49–50
Medical supplies, needed by physician, 157–166
Medical witnesses, expert, 248–249
Medicolegal investigations, 245–246
Menninger, William C., 39–40
Microbiology, 47
Military obligation, 129
Modern Drug Encyclopedia and Therapeutic Index, 165
Modern Drugs, 165
Morgagni, Giovanni Battista, 4
Morphine, prescription regulations, 163
Morphological concept of disease, 4
Municipal departments, dealings with, 20
Myocardial infarction, 94–95

Narcotics, prescription regulations, 162–163, 246–247
National Association of Clinic Managers, 86–87
National Board of Medical Examiners, 106
Neurological Surgery, American Board of, 107
Neurology, 45, 62
New and Nonofficial Remedies, 165

New England Journal of Medicine, 60–61

Nurse: relations with patient and physician, 119–121; as medical assistant, 178

OBSTETRICS, 45, 62

Obstetrics and Gynecology, American Board of, 70, 107

Office, doctor's: assistants, 29, 177–181, 188–199; location, 46–47, 63, 66, 176; supplies and equipment, 158–162; related business aspects, 167–176; initial costs, 172; rent, 218

Office laboratory. *See* Laboratory

Ophthalmology, 45

Ophthalmology, American Board of, 70, 107

Opium derivatives, prescription regulations, 163

Opportunities: for practice of medicine, 38–47; academic work, 47–49; public health work, 49; medical statesmanship, 49–50

Organizations: nonmedical, 21–23; wife's membership in, 27; medical, 109–115

Orthopaedic Surgery, American Board of, 107

Orthopedics, 45

Osler, William, 4, 132

Otolaryngology, 45

Otolaryngology, American Board of, 108

Otology, American Board of, 70

Outpatient clinics: doctor's duty to, 98–99; research opportunities, 102

Outside calls, 206

Owner's, landlord's and tenant's liability insurance, 232

PARTNERSHIPS, 81–82, 243

Pathology, 48, 74

Pathology, American Board of, 108

Patients: handling of calls of, 181–183; day book record of, 192–194; record of, 194–195, 198; and bills, 199–204

Patients' ledger, 208

Payroll book, 215

Pediatrics, 43, 62

Pediatrics, American Board of, 108

Percussion, 4

Periodicals, professional, 133

Personal liability insurance, 232–233

Personal life, community demands on, 15

Personal physician, 51. *See also* Generalist

Personnel. *See* Assistants, medical or office

Personnel Institute, New York, 180

Petty cash book, 212–213

Pharmaceutical houses, 164

Pharmacist, 159–160

Pharmacology, 47

Pharmacy, 157

Pharmacy and Chemistry, Council on (A.M.A.), 112, 165

Physical Medicine and Rehabilitation, American Board of, 108

Physician: qualities necessary in, 6, 41, 42; responsibilities of, 12;

meaning of term, 41; as writer, 137–138; relationship with patient, 252–253

Physician's Desk Reference, 165

Physiology, 4, 5, 47

Plastic Surgery, American Board of, 108

Post-mortem examinations, 99–100, 256–257

Practice: urban, 53–54; suburban, 54–55; small-city, 56; semi-rural, 56–58; rural, 59; group, 64; introduction to, 74–76; and economic security, 242–243

Preclinical sciences, 47

Prescription blanks, 159, 162

Prescriptions, 159–160, 162–163

Preventive medicine, 117

Preventive Medicine, American Board of, 108

Principles of Ethics of the American Medical Association, 184, 252

Proctology, 45

Proctology, American Board of, 108

Property insurance, 233–234

Psychiatrist, 39, 43–44

Psychiatry, 43–44, 62

Psychiatry and Neurology, American Board of, 108

Psychological Corporation, New York, 180

Public health: physician's services in, 19–24; opportunities in, 49; municipal facilities, 124–125; county, 125–126; state, 126

Public Health Service. *See* U.S. Public Health Service

Public welfare board, 116–117

Purchasing, of office equipment, 173–175

Quarterly Cumulative Index Medicus, 136

RADIOLOGY, 45, 74

Radiology, American Board of, 108

Reading clubs, 104–105

Reagents, laboratory, 143

Real estate investment, 229–230

Reception room, 168

Records: office, 191–204; patients', 194–195, 198; cash basis method, 206–208

Red Cross, 22, 27

Referral, income and expense, 216

Refresher courses, 166

Registered nurse, as assistant, 178

Rent, office, 218

Repairs, 221–222

Repertoire, laboratory, 146; recent contributions to, 149–150

Res ipsa loquitur doctrine, 251

Research: medical, 39; clinical, 48–49

Residencies, 64

Resident specialist, 74

Rural Health, Council on (A.M.A.), 111

Rural medical care, 47

Rural practice, 59

Rusk, Howard A., 14

SALAMANCA, UNIVERSITY OF, 6

Salaries, deductions for, 217

Saturday Review, 7

Scales, for doctor's office, 158

Security, economic, 226–244

Semirural practice, 56–58
"Service" ward, 99–100, 102
Small-city practice, 56
Social activities, 22
Socialized medicine, 99
Societies and associations, medical, 109–115
Specialist: 139; function of, 42; vs. generalist, 46–47, 71–72; necessity for, 67–68; training, 73–74; introduction to practice, 74–76; office equipment needs, 172–173
Specialization, 69
Specialties: clinical, 45; nonoperative, 45; subclinical, 74
Specialty boards: first organized, 68; concern for increasing specialties, 69; objectives, 70; requirements of, 105–106; organizations approving, 105–106; qualifications required by, 107; members of, 107–108. *Individual boards listed under field of specialization*
Specialty practice, 67–76
Sperry, Willard, 10
State and Territory Health Authorities, Directory of, 152
State departments of health, relations with, 20; requirements of, 117
State medical society, 110–111
State statutes, 247
Stocks, investment advice, 229–230
Subclinical specialties, 74
Subspecialties, certification, 108
Suburban practice, 54–55
Supplies, medical and office, 157–166, 223
Surgeon: 39; meaning of term, 41; qualities necessary in, 41–42
Surgery, 74–76
Surgery, American Board of, 69, 73–74, 108
Surgical equipment, for doctor's bag, 161–162
Sydenham, Thomas, 5
Symptomatic therapy, 154

TAX EXPENSE, 219
Tax savings factors, 240–242
Technical advances, 3–5
Technics, laboratory, 150–151
Telephone: handling of, 181–183; answering service, 185
Telephone and telegraph expense, 223
Therapy: symptomatic, 154; drug, 163–166
Thoracic surgeon, 69
Thoracic Surgery, American Board of, 70, 108
Towel service, 159
Training: for clinical specialties, 45; for specialists, 68–69, 73–74; for medical assistants, 180–181
Transportation, 175–176
Trauma, 73–74
Traveling expense, 223
Treatment, generalist's responsibilities in, 62
Treatment rooms, 169–172
Trustee, corporate, 230
Trusts, 239

U.S. BUREAU OF NARCOTICS, 246
U.S. *Pharmacopoeia,* 165

U.S. Public Health Service: Clinical Center, 49; on group practice, 79; services of, 126–127; directory of public health authorities, 152
Urban practice, 53–54
Urologist, 69
Urology, 45
Urology, American Board of, 108
Utility expense, deductions for, 224

VACATIONS, 19
Veterans' Administration: relations with, 20; cases to refer to, 116–117; procedure with, 126–128
Visiting nursing associations, 22

Voluntary agencies and associations, 21–22, 123

WAGES: of medical assistants, 181; deductions for, 217
Wife, doctor's, 15–18, 25–37
Wills and trusts, 239–240
Witnesses, expert medical, 248–249
Work week: 14; of specialist vs. general practitioner, 71–72
Workmen's compensation insurance, 232

X-RAY EXAMINATIONS, early use of, 4

Year Book of Drug Therapy, 166